Trails to Explore

Second Edition

A Beka Book® Pensacol
an affiliate of PENSACOLA CHRISTIA

D0954914

To Parents and Teachers

Children are eagerly searching for a workable sense of values. They need reading material that will give them ideals to reach for and examples to follow.

The stories in this reader have been selected from the readers of America's past and have been edited, modernized, and classroom-tested for student appeal and readability. Many character values are woven throughout the stories. Thought questions at the end of the stories aid in understanding the selections.

Trails to Explore
Second Edition

Staff Credits

Editors: Laurel Hicks, Marion Hedquist
Designer: Michelle Johnson
Illustrators: Brian Jekel, Stan Shimmin, Matthew Sample II, and staff

Copyright © 2008, 1998 Pensacola Christian College
All rights reserved. Printed in U.S.A.

Credits appear on pages 392–393 which are considered an extension of copyright page.

No part of this publication may be reproduced or transmitted in any form or by any means, electronic or mechanical, including photocopy, recording, or any information storage and retrieval system, or by license from any collective or licensing body, without permission in writing from the publisher.

Cataloging Data
    Trails to explore / editors: Laurel Hicks, Marion Hedquist.
        393 p. : col. ill. ; 22 cm. (A Beka Book reading program)
    1. Readers (Primary) 2. Reading (Primary) III. Hicks, Laurel.
IV. Hedquist, Marion. V. A Beka Book, Inc.
Library of Congress PE1119 .T73 2008
Dewey System 428.6

CONTENTS

UNIT 1

Amazing Animals

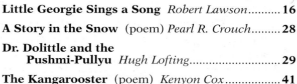

We Invent the Franklin
Stove *Robert Lawson*............2

Bobo *Elizabeth O. Jones*.............8

Little Georgie Sings a Song *Robert Lawson*..........16

A Story in the Snow (poem) *Pearl R. Crouch*.........28

**Dr. Dolittle and the
Pushmi-Pullyu** *Hugh Lofting*............29

The Kangarooster (poem) *Kenyon Cox*.................41

Wilbur Meets Charlotte *E. B. White*......................42

Farms (poem) *Eleanor Farjeon*.................60

A Dragon-fly (poem) *Eleanor Farjeon*.....................62

Captain Cook *Richard & Florence Atwater*..............63

Duck's Ditty (poem) *Kenneth Grahame*..................75

Seal (poem) *William J. Smith*.................76

UNIT 2

The Way West

Whitey and Jinglebob *Glen Rounds*......................78

Go West, Young Man (poem) *Dorothy Hall*..........90

The Cowboy's Life (poem) *James B. Adams*..........91

Andy Stands Guard *Stanley Young*.......................92

Our Native Land (poem) *C. T. Brooks*.................102

No Other Land (poem) *James G. Percival*.......103

Tall Bram of Little Pigeon
Manly W. Wellman.........................104

Abraham Lincoln (poem)
Mildred P. Meigs.....................120

Dan Drake's First Patient
Marion Renick/ Margaret C. Tyler......... 121

Yukon Trail *Willis Lindquist*.....................132

**Stopping by Woods on a
Snowy Evening** (poem)
Robert Frost.............................145

Kapiolani the Brave *Hugh T. Kerr* 146

Two Thousand Miles for a Book
Cynthia P. Maus.....................153

UNIT 3

Friends & Neighbors

The Heart Test Sandra Klaus 160

I'm Not Alone (poem) L. E. Dunkin 168

The Old Indian Trail Lillie V. Albrecht 169

Winner Take a Mule E. H. Lansing 175

Our Heroes (poem)
Alice & Phoebe Cary 185

The Middle Bear Eleanor Estes 186

Furry Bear (poem) A. A. Milne 207

Citronella Weather
Mildred Lawrence 208

The President's Whiskers
Hertha Pauli 221

The Willow Basket
Carol Ryrie Brink 233

My Daily Creed (poem) Author Unknown 249

UNIT 4

Well-Loved Tales

God's Trees Helen F. Bower 250

Through His Name (poem)
Author Unknown 259

Dick Whittington and
His Cat James Baldwin 260

Cats (poem) Eleanor Farjeon 275

Cat (poem) Mary B. Miller 276

The Elephant's Child Rudyard Kipling 277

The Elephant (poem) Hilaire Belloc 290

The Hippopotamus (poem)
Georgia R. Durston 290

Habits of the Hippopotamus
(poem) Arthur Guiterman 292

Paul Bunyan, Northwoods
Lumberman Walter Blair 293

Mary Indoors (poem) Eleanor Farjeon ... 301

The Legend of William Tell
Amy Cruse 302

UNIT 5

In Other Lands

We Understand So Little *Jewish Folktale* 310

Knowledge (poem) *Eleanor Farjeon* 314

The Book Lost at Sea *Hugh T. Kerr* 315

Thy Word (poem) *Author Unknown*.................. 320

Moni and His Goats *Johanna Spyri* 321

I Stood Alone (poem) *G. Kearnie Keegan* 330

The Persian and His Sons *William J. Sly* 331

True Nobility (poem) *Edgar Guest* 334

**Robinson Crusoe's
New Home** *Daniel Defoe*............................ 335

UNIT 6

People to Meet

The Greatest River in the World
  Catherine O. Peare... 346

Ahoy, There! (poem) *Dorothy Hall*.................... 355

Battle with Death *Dorothy Haas* 356

**Something Really
Important** *Lee H. Mountain*........................ 367

Because of Thy Great Bounty (poem)
  Grace N. Crowell 378

Lift Off *Gene Gurney*... 380

Credits **392**

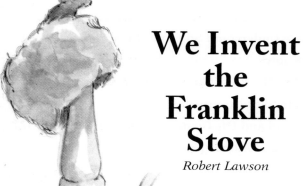

We Invent the Franklin Stove

Robert Lawson

During the hard winter of 1745, Amos the church mouse found shelter in the home of Ben Franklin. Here is part of Amos's story, telling how he became Ben's "closest friend and advisor and, if I do say it, in great part responsible for his success and fame." This story is from *Ben and Me,* an enjoyable book by the author of *Rabbit Hill.*

I slept late the next morning. When I woke my fur-cap home was hanging on the bedpost, and I in it.

Dr. Franklin was again crouched over the fire attempting to write, between fits of sneezing and glasses-hunting. The fire, what there was of it, was smoking, and the room was as cold as ever.

"Not wishing to be critical—" I said. "But, perhaps, a bit of wood on that smoky ember that you seem to consider a fire might—"

"WASTE NOT, WANT NOT," said he, severely, and went on writing.

---

critical—*finding fault; judgmental*

ember—*a glowing piece of coal or wood from a fire*

"Well, just suppose," I said, "just suppose you spend two or three weeks in bed with pewmonia— would that be a waste or—"

"It would be," said he, putting on a log; "whatever your name might be."

"Amos," said I. . . . "And then there'd be doctors' bills—"

"BILLS!" said he, shuddering, and put on two more logs, quick. The fire blazed up then, and the room became a little better, but not much.

"Dr. Franklin," I said, "that fireplace is all wrong."

"You might call me Ben—just plain Ben," said he. . . . "What's wrong with it?"

"Well, for one thing, most of the heat goes up the chimney. And for another, you can't get *around* it. Now, outside our church there used to be a Hot-chestnut Man. Sometimes, when business was rushing, he'd drop a chestnut. Pop was always on the lookout, and almost before it touched the ground he'd have it in his sack—and down to the vestry with it. There he'd put it in the middle of the floor—and we'd all gather round for the warmth.

---

vestry—*a small room in a church used for choir robes, prayer meetings, etc.*

"Twenty-eight of us it would heat, and the room as well. It was all because it was OUT IN THE OPEN, not stuck in a hole in the wall like that fireplace."

"Amos," he interrupts, excited, "there's an idea there! But we couldn't move the fire out into the middle of the room."

"We could if there were something to put it in, iron or something."

"But the smoke?" he objected.

"PIPE," said I, and curled up for another nap. I didn't get it, though.

Ben rushed off downstairs, came back with a great armful of junk, dumped it on the floor and was off for more. No one could have slept, not even a dormouse. After a few trips he had a big pile of things there. There were scraps of iron, tin and wire. There were a couple of old warming pans, an iron oven, three flatirons, six pot-lids, a wire birdcage and an anvil. There were saws, hammers, pincers, files, drills, nails, screws, bolts, bricks, sand, and an old broken sword.

---

warming pan—*a long-handled, covered pan that could hold live coals and be used to warm a bed*
flatiron—*a piece of iron that was heated in a fire and used for pressing clothes*
anvil—*an iron or steel block on which a blacksmith places metal objects for hammering into shape*
pincers—*a tool used for gripping or nipping things*

He drew out a sort of plan and went to work. With the clatter he made there was no chance of a nap, so I helped all I could, picking up the nuts and screws and tools that he dropped—and his glasses.

Ben was a fair terror for work, once he was interested. It was almost noon before he stopped for a bit of rest. We looked over what had been done and it didn't look so bad—considering.

It was shaped much like a small fireplace set up on legs, with two iron doors on the front and a smoke pipe running from the back to the fireplace. He had taken the andirons out of the fireplace and boarded that up so we wouldn't lose any heat up the chimney.

Ben walked around looking at it, proud as could be, but worried.

---

andirons—*the two metal pieces that hold the wood in a fireplace*

"The floor," he says. "It's the floor that troubles me, Amos. With those short legs and that thin iron bottom, the heat—"

"Down on the docks," said I, "we used to hear the ship-rats telling how the sailors build their cooking fires on board ship. A layer of sand right on the deck, bricks on top of that, and—"

"Amos," he shouts, "you've got it!" and rushed for the bricks and sand. He put a layer of sand in the bottom of the affair, the bricks on top of that, and then set the andirons in.

It looked pretty promising.

"Eureka!" he exclaims, stepping back to admire it—and tripping over the saw. "Straighten things up a bit, Amos, while I run and get some logs."

"*Don't* try to run," I said. "And by the way, do you come through the pantry on the way up?"

"Why?" he asked.

"In some ways, Ben," I said, "you're fairly bright, but in others you're just plain dull. The joy of creating may be meat and drink to you; but as for me, a bit of cheese—"

He was gone before I finished, but when he came back with the logs he did have a fine slab of cheese and a loaf of rye bread.

We put in some kindling and logs and lit her up. She drew fine, and Ben was so proud and excited that I had to be rather sharp with him before he would settle down to food. Even then he was up every minute, to admire it from a new angle.

Before we'd finished even one sandwich, the room had warmed up like a summer afternoon.

"Amos," says he, "we've done it!"

"Thanks for the WE," I said. "I'll remember it."

---

kindling—*small pieces of wood used to start a fire*

Character Theme—Resourcefulness

Thinking It Through

1. What character in this story is real, and which is imaginary?
2. How could you tell that Ben was cold?
3. Why would *not* putting more wood on the fire be wasteful?
4. Where did a fire need to be, if it was going to heat the entire room?
5. Who wanted to be given credit for inventing the stove?

Bobo

Elizabeth Orton Jones

I first came upon Bobo one day when I was out walking on a country road. I was going slowly along, thinking of nothing in particular, when I happened to look down at my feet. And there, not three inches away—wasn't it lucky that I hadn't stepped on him?—was a baby bird.

He was a tiny thing, and quite bare, except for a few pinfeathers pricking through. His skin, which looked a few sizes too large for him, was all wrinkly and purplish. In fact, he was rather an ugly baby.

---

pinfeather—*a growing feather still covered with a horny material and just emerging through the skin*

"Oh," I thought, "he must be a baby bluejay. That's just what he must be!"

I had heard, of course, that the first thing you ought to do after finding a baby bird on the ground is to look for the nest from which he has fallen. So I looked up into the tree above and nearly turned a backwards somersault trying to see into the highest branches. I could see no nest at all. From where had he come?

I looked at his funny, ugly little face. "Hello, Bobo!" I said.

His beak was very yellow and big. He opened it wide and a loud squawk came out of him—a *very* loud squawk for such a baby!

I held Bobo high up with my hand, so that his parents might see him, should they be anywhere around. But if they were there, they took no notice.

I tried putting him up in the crotch of the tree. But he fell down again and flopped over into the road.

In the end, I decided to take him home with me. There seemed to be no two ways about it. So I made my hands into the shape of a little house for Bobo, and I started off down the road toward home.

But oh, all of a sudden I thought of Petey! He is my cat, a very proud Persian. He has long, silvery fur and a bright pink nose and large, shiny green eyes. Of course, he was only a kitten then. But just the same, I had heard tales of what kittens might do to little birds!

So, you may be sure, I was very careful to keep them apart. At night, I locked Petey out of my room, while I slept with Bobo beside me on the pillow, cuddled up against my neck to keep him warm. I was afraid of rolling over on him and so used to keep waking up every once in awhile to make sure he was still alive.

But one morning I found that I had evidently been sleeping more soundly than usual. Bobo was safe and perfectly happy in his place beside my neck. But Petey was fast asleep on the other side of the pillow. The door, strangely enough, stood wide open.

Well, just to see what would happen, I put Bobo over close beside the sleeping Petey. With a yawn and a purr, Petey awoke and began to lick Bobo. He gave him a good washing, up his little breast and down his back. Then he put his pink nose up against Bobo's funny little wing. I dare say that was his way of kissing Bobo.

At any rate, Petey and Bobo became good friends.

When Bobo was old enough to hop about, he used to pretend that Petey was a hill and would climb up onto his back. And Petey used to pretend that Bobo was a ball and would roll him around with his paws—very gently, of course. Then, when the hill and the ball felt tired of play, they would go to sleep together.

After Bobo had grown some feathers, Petey used to wash them with his tongue very carefully every day. And Bobo, to return the kindness, would preen Petey's long tail with his beak.

Bobo loved other kinds of baths, too. He had his own bathtub, of course. But if a cup of tea

---

preen—*to smooth or clean with the beak*

were left standing, Bobo was sure to take a bath
in it. Or a dish of soup, or a pitcher of cream, or
a glass of ginger ale—all would be bathed in by
Bobo at the first opportunity. He was really very
naughty. I couldn't scold him, because he loved
to be scolded and would squawk with joy each
time I began. And I couldn't very well spank
him because, somehow, it didn't seem quite right

to spank a bird. If you've ever tried it, I dare say you've found out what a brute it makes you feel. However, in the end, Bobo punished himself. One day I found him flopping about in a jar of honey. Oh, he was a sticky bird that day! And he had to be given still another kind of bath, a very splashy one, under the faucet. And after that he was a little more careful about what he bathed in.

Day by day and week by week Bobo grew larger, until he had grown into quite a large bird. He had been an ugly baby, but as his bright feathers grew, he became more and more beautiful. He never had more than two or three feathers in his tail, to be sure, for Petey had a way of sitting on Bobo's tail just when he was about to fly away. But I thought he was beautiful even without a full set of tail feathers!

Little by little Bobo learned how to fly. And when he was able to fly very well, then I knew that he was old enough to go into the woods and fend for himself.

So, very sadly one day, I walked far into the woods, carrying Bobo in my hands. I said good-bye to him and let him go. He flew up into the top of a tree.

"Be happy, Bobo!" I called to him.

Then, very sadly, I started back.

And what do you think I saw when I got home?

Petey was lying on the doorstep sound asleep in the sun. And between his paws slept Bobo, looking as if nothing at all had happened!

After that, of course, Bobo stayed with us.

When he was very young, I used to feed him bread and milk which I stuffed down his throat with the end of a match. How he squawked and flapped his funny little wings as each bite went down! I soon learned that he expected a large dinner just about every hour. And I used to think how pleasant it would be, the day when Bobo was old enough to feed himself.

But that day never came. Even when he was a grown-up bird, do you think he ever caught a grasshopper for himself? Not he. He just sat squawking and flapping his wings over the place where a grasshopper was. And I had to catch the grasshopper for him!

Bobo loved to go with me wherever I went. When he was a little bird, he used to hop along after me, upstairs and downstairs and into the garden. Then, after he knew how to fly, he used to go down to the village with me, flying along from tree to tree, squawking with joy as he went.

14

The end of summer came all too soon, and the time to go back into the city. I knew that something would have to be done about Bobo. The city was no place for a bluejay. So I gave him to a very kind man who loved birds. And, for all I know, Bobo is living there still, probably taking baths in the kind man's teacup!

Character Theme—Friendship

Thinking It Through

1. What things did the writer do to try to get the bird back to its parents?
2. How did Bobo learn his lesson not to bathe in any liquid he could find?
3. When did Bobo learn to feed himself?
4. What was so unusual about Petey's friendship with Bobo?

Little Georgie Sings a Song

Robert Lawson

New folks are coming to live in the big house on Rabbit Hill, and to the animals that brings the hope of a good garden and good eating. No one is more excited than Little Georgie Rabbit, who is sent to tell Uncle Analdas the news, in spite of his mother's uneasiness about him going alone. You can read more of the adventures of the small animals in *Rabbit Hill,* by Robert Lawson.

It was barely daylight when Little Georgie started his journey. In spite of her worrying, Mother had managed to put up a small but nourishing lunch. This, along with a letter to Uncle Analdas, was packed in a little knapsack and slung over his shoulder. Father went along was far as the Twin Bridges. As they stepped briskly down the Hill the whole valley was a lake of mist on which rounded treetops swam like floating islands. From old orchards rose a

Analdas (ə·năl′dŭs)   nourishing—*healthy*

mounting chorus as the birds greeted the new day. Mothers chirped and chuckled and scolded as they swept and tidied the nests. On the topmost branches their menfolk warbled and shrilled and mocked one another.

The houses were all asleep, even the Dogs of the Fat-Man-at-the-Crossroads were quiet, but the Little Animals were up and about. They met the Gray Fox returning from a night up Weston way. He looked footsore and sleepy, and a few chicken feathers still clung to his ruff. The Red Buck trotted daintily across the Black Road to wish them good luck and good morning, but Father, for once, had no time for long social conversation. This was business, and no Rabbit in the county knew his business any better than Father—few as well.

"Now, son," he said firmly, "your mother is in a very nervous state and you are not to add to her worries by taking unnecessary risks or by carelessness. No dawdling and no foolishness. Keep close to the road but well off it. Watch your bridges and your crossings. What do you do when you come to a bridge?"

"I hide well," answered Georgie, "and wait a good long time. I look all around for Dogs. I look up the road for cars and down the road for cars.

---

dawdling—*wasting time*

When everything's clear I run across—fast. I hide again and look around to be sure I've not been seen. Then I go on. The same thing for crossings."

"Good," said Father. "Now recite your Dogs."

Little Georgie closed his eyes and dutifully recited, "Fat-Man-at-the-Crossroads: two Mongrels; Good Hill Road: Dalmatian; house on Long Hill: Collie, noisy, no wind; Norfield Church corner: Police Dog, stupid, no nose; On the High Ridge, red farmhouse: Bulldog and Setter, both fat, don't bother; farmhouse with the big barns: Old Hound, very dangerous . . ." and so on. He recited every dog on the route clear up to Danbury way. He did it without a mistake and swelled with pride at Father's approving nod.

"Excellent," said Father. "Now do you remember your checks and doublings?" Little Georgie closed his eyes again and rattled off, quite fast, "Sharp right and double left, double left and double right, dead stop and back flip, right jump, left jump, false trip, and briar dive."

"Splendid," said Father. "Now attend carefully. Size up your Dog; don't waste speed on a plodder, you may need it later. If he's a rusher, check, double, and freeze. Your freeze, by the way, is still

---

mongrel—*a dog of mixed breed*
check—*a sudden stop*

attend—*to pay close attention to*

18

rather bad. You have a tendency to flick your left ear; you must watch that. The High Ridge is very open country so keep in the shadow of the stone walls and mark the earth piles. Porkey [the wood-chuck] has lots of relatives along there, and if you are pressed hard any of them will gladly take you in. Just tell them who you are, and don't forget to thank them. After a chase, hide up and take at least ten minutes' rest. And if you have to *really* run, tighten that knapsack strap, lace back your ears, put your stomach to the ground, and RUN!

"Get along with you now, and mind—no fool-ishness. We shall expect you and Uncle Analdas by tomorrow evening at the latest."

Little Georgie crossed the Twin Bridges in per-fect form, returned Father's approving wave, and was off on his own.

It was gray and misty as he crossed Good Hill Road, and the Dalmatian still slept. So, apparently, did the Collie up the road, for all was quiet as he plodded up Long Hill. People were beginning to stir as he approached Norfield Church corner; lit-tle plumes of blue smoke were rising from kitchen chimneys, and the air was pleasant with the smell of frying bacon.

---

plumes—*clouds resembling feathers*

As he expected, the
Police Dog rushed him there, but he wasted little
time on that affair. Loping along with tantalizing slowness until they were almost on an old
fallen apple tree buried in briars, he executed a
dead stop, a right jump, and a freeze. The bel-
lowing brute over-ran him and plunged headlong
into the thorny tangle. His agonized howls were
sweet music to Little Georgie as he hopped sedately along toward the High Ridge. He wished
Father had been there to see how skillfully he had
worked and to note that during the freeze his left
ear hadn't flickered once.

The sun was well up when he emerged on the
High Ridge. On the porch of the red farmhouse
the fat Bulldog and the Setter slept soundly, soaking up its warmth. On any other occasion Little

tantalizing—*teasing* sedately—*quietly; calmly*
execute—*to carry out; do* emerge—*to come out*

Georgie would have been tempted to wake them to enjoy their silly efforts at running, but, mindful of Father's instructions, he kept dutifully on his way.

The High Ridge was a long and open strip of country, very uninteresting to Little Georgie. The view, over miles and miles of rolling woods and meadows, was very beautiful, but he didn't care especially about views. The brilliant blue sky and the bright little cream-puff clouds were beautiful too. They made him feel good; so did the warm sun, but frankly he was becoming slightly bored. So to ease his boredom he began to make a little song.

The words had been rattling around in his head for some days now, and the music was there too, but he couldn't quite get them straight and fitted together. So he hummed and he sang and he whistled. He tried the words this way and that way, he stopped and started and changed the notes around, and finally he got the first line so that it suited him. So Georgie sang that line over and over again to be sure that he wouldn't forget it when he started on the second line.

It must have been this preoccupation with his song that made Little Georgie careless and almost

---

preoccupation—*distraction*

21

led to his undoing. He scarcely noticed that he
had passed the house with the big barns, and he
was just starting to sing his first line for the forty-
seventh time when there came the roaring rush of
the Old Hound right on his heels, so close that he
could feel the hot breath.

Instinctively Little Georgie made several wild
springs that carried him temporarily out of harm's
way. He paused a fraction of a second to tighten
the knapsack strap and then set off at a good
steady pace. "Don't waste speed on a plodder" was
Father's rule. He tried a few checks and doubles
and circlings, although he knew they were pretty
useless. The great fields were too bare, and the
Old Hound knew all the tricks. No matter how he
turned and dodged, the Hound was always there,
coming along at his heavy gallop. He looked for
Woodchuck burrows, but there were none in sight.
"Well, I guess I'll have to run it out," said Little
Georgie.

He pulled the knapsack strap tighter, laced
back his ears, put his stomach to the ground, and
RAN. And *how* he ran!

The warm sun had loosened his muscles; the
air was invigorating; Little Georgie's leaps grew

---

instinctively—*naturally, without having to think*
invigorate—*to fill with energy*

longer and longer. Never had he felt so young and strong. His legs were like coiled springs of steel that released themselves of their own accord. He was hardly conscious of any effort, only of his hind feet pounding the ground, and each time they hit, those wonderful springs released and shot him through the air. He sailed over fences and stone walls as though they were mole runs. Why, this was almost like flying! Now he understood what Zip the Swallow had been driving at when he tried to describe what it was like. He glanced back at the Old Hound, far behind now, but still coming along at his plodding gallop. He was old and must be tiring, while he, Little Georgie, felt stronger and more vigorous at every leap. Why didn't the old fool give up and go home?

And then, as he shot over the brow of a slight rise, he suddenly knew. *He had forgotten Dead-man's Brook!* There it lay before him, broad and deep, curving out in a great silvery loop. He, the son of Father, gentleman hunter from the Blue-grass, had been driven into a trap, a trap that even Porkey should have been able to avoid! Whether he turned to right or left the loop of the creek hemmed him in and the Old Hound could easily cut him off. There was nothing for it but to jump!

---

vigorous—*energetic, strong*

23

This sickening realization had not
reduced his speed; now he redoubled it.
The slope helped, and his soaring leaps became
prodigious. The wind whistled through his laced-
back ears. Still he kept his head, as Father would
have wished him to. He picked a spot where the
bank was high and firm; he spaced his jumps so
they would come out exactly right.

The take-off was perfect. He put every ounce
of leg muscle into that final kick and sailed out
into space. Below him he could see the cream-
puff clouds mirrored in the dark water, he could
see the pebbles on the bottom and the silver flash
of frightened minnows dashing away from his
flying shadow. Then, with a breath-taking thump,
he landed, turned seven somersaults, and came
up sitting in a clump of soft lush grass.

He froze, motionless except for heaving sides,

---

prodigious—*great; enormous*

and watched the Old Hound come thundering down the slope, slide to a stop and, after eyeing the water disgustedly, take his way slowly homeward, his dripping tongue almost dragging the ground.

Little Georgie did not need to remember Father's rule for a ten-minute rest after a good run. He was blown and he knew it, but he did remember his lunch, so he unstrapped the little knapsack and combined lunch and rest. He had been really scared for a moment, but as his wind came back and his lunch went down, his spirits came up.

Father would be angry, and rightly, for he had made two very stupid mistakes: he had let himself

25

be surprised, and he had run right into a dangerous trap. But that leap! Never in the history of
the county had any rabbit jumped Deadman's
Brook, not even Father. He marked the exact
spot and calculated the width of the stream
there—at least eighteen feet! And with his rising
spirits the words and the notes of his song suddenly tumbled into place.

Little Georgie lay back in the warm grass and
sang his song—

> New Folks coming, oh my!
> New Folks coming, oh my!
> New Folks coming, oh my!
> Oh my! Oh my!

---

calculated—*figured out*

Character Theme—Attentiveness

Thinking It Through

1. What happened while Georgie was making up a song?

2. What did Georgie do that he knew would disappoint his father?

3. What wonderful thing did he do?

4. Why was it very important for Georgie to attend to his father's instructions?

 *From the Bible*

My son, attend unto my wisdom, and bow thine ear to my understanding.
—*Proverbs 5:1*

Honor thy father and thy mother: that thy days may be long upon the land which the Lord thy God giveth thee.
—*Exodus 20:12*

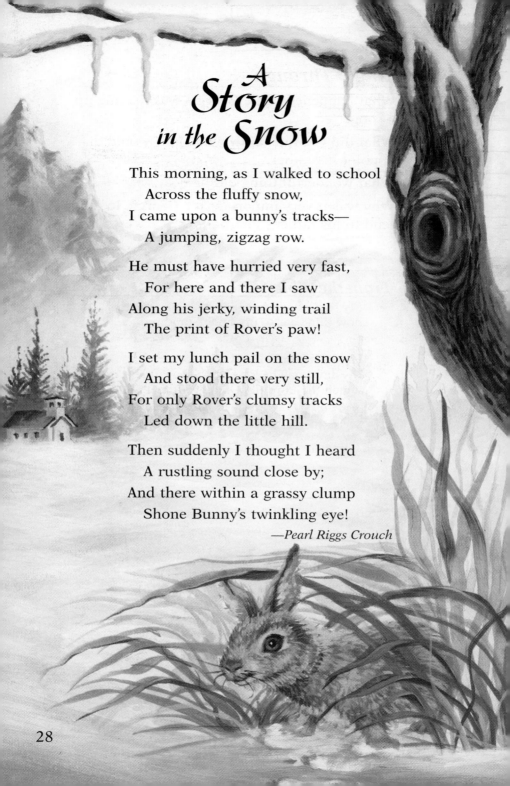

A Story in the Snow

This morning, as I walked to school
    Across the fluffy snow,
I came upon a bunny's tracks—
    A jumping, zigzag row.

He must have hurried very fast,
    For here and there I saw
Along his jerky, winding trail
    The print of Rover's paw!

I set my lunch pail on the snow
    And stood there very still,
For only Rover's clumsy tracks
    Led down the little hill.

Then suddenly I thought I heard
    A rustling sound close by;
And there within a grassy clump
    Shone Bunny's twinkling eye!

—*Pearl Riggs Crouch*

Dr. Dolittle and the Pushmi-Pullyu

from *The Story of Doctor Dolittle*
Hugh Lofting

Dr. John Dolittle was no ordinary animal doctor. He was so devoted to his patients that he learned their languages. When Chee-Chee, his pet monkey, told him of a terrible sickness among the monkeys of Africa, Dr. Dolittle and his animal friends went to Africa to help out. But now the good doctor has an important reason for returning to his home in Puddleby-on-the-Marsh.

John Dolittle told the monkeys that he must now go back to Puddleby.

They were very surprised at this; for they had thought that he was going to stay with them forever. And that day all the monkeys got together in the jungle to talk it over.

And the Chief Chimpanzee rose up and said,

"Why is it the good man is going away? Is he not happy here with us?"

But none of them could answer him.

Then the
Grand Gorilla got up and said,
    "I think we should all go to him
and ask him to stay. Perhaps if we make him a
new house and a bigger bed, and promise him
plenty of monkey servants to work for him and to
make life pleasant for him—perhaps then he will
not wish to go."

    Then Chee-Chee got up, and all the others
whispered, "Sh! Look! Chee-Chee, the great Traveler, is about to speak!"

    And Chee-Chee said to the other monkeys,
"My friends, I am afraid it is useless to ask the

Doctor to stay. He owes money in Puddleby; and he says he must go back and pay it."

And the monkeys asked him, "What is *money?*"

Then Chee-Chee told them that in the Land of the White Men you could get nothing without money; you could *do* nothing without money—that it was almost impossible to *live* without money.

And some of them asked, "But can you not even eat and drink without paying?"

But Chee-Chee shook his head. And then he told them that even he, when he was with the organ-grinder, had been made to ask the children for money.

And the Chief Chimpanzee turned to the Oldest Orangutan and said, "Cousin, surely these Men be strange creatures! Who would wish to live in such a land? My gracious, how paltry!"

Then Chee-Chee said, "When we were coming to you, we had no boat to cross the sea in and no money to buy food to eat on our journey. So a man lent us some biscuits; and we said we would pay him when we came back. And we borrowed a boat from a sailor; but it was broken on the rocks when we reached the shores of Africa. Now the Doctor says he must go back and get the sailor

---

orangutan (ô·răng′ə·tăn)—
  a large ape with shaggy, reddish-
  brown hair and very long arms

paltry—*practically
  worthless*

another boat—because the man was poor and his ship was all he had."

And the monkeys were all silent for a while, sitting quite still and thinking hard.

At last the Biggest Baboon got up and said, "I do not think we ought to let this good man leave our land till we have given him a fine present to take with him, so that he may know we are grateful for all that he has done for us."

And a little, tiny red monkey who was sitting up in a tree shouted down,

"I think that, too!"

And then they all cried out, making a great noise, "Yes, yes. Let us give him the finest present a White Man ever had!"

Now they began to wonder and to ask one another what would be the best thing to give him. And one said, "Fifty bags of coconuts!" And another—"A hundred bunches of bananas! At least he shall not have to buy his fruit in the Land Where You Pay To Eat!"

But Chee-Chee told them that all these things would be too heavy to carry so far and would go bad before half was eaten.

"If you want to please him," he said, "give him an animal. You may be sure he will be kind to it. Give him some rare animal they have not got in the menageries."

And the monkeys asked him, "What are menageries?"

Then Chee-Chee explained to them that menageries were places in the Land of the White Men, where animals were put in cages for people to come and look at. And the monkeys were very shocked, and said to one another,

"These Men are like thoughtless young ones— foolish and easily amused. Sh! It is a prison he means."

So then they asked Chee-Chee what rare animal it could be that they should give the Doctor— one the White Men had not seen before. And the Major of the Marmosets asked,

"Have they an iguana over there?"

But Chee-Chee said, "Yes, there is one in the London Zoo."

And another asked, "Have they an okapi?"

But Chee-Chee said, "Yes. In Belgium, where my organ-grinder took me five years ago, they had an okapi in a big city they call Antwerp."

And another asked, "Have they a pushmi-pullyu?"

---

menagerie (mə·năj′ə·rē)—*a zoo; collection of unusual animals*
marmoset—*a small monkey with thick, soft hair*

okapi (ō·kä′pē)—*an African animal similar to a giraffe, but with a much shorter neck*

33

Then Chee-Chee said, "No. No White Man has ever seen a pushmi-pullyu. Let us give him that."

A Strange Beast

Pushmi-pullyus are now extinct. That means there aren't any more. But long ago, when Doctor Dolittle was alive, there were some of them still left in the deepest jungles of Africa; and even then they were very, very scarce. They had no tail, but a head at each end, and sharp horns on each head. They were very shy and terribly hard to catch. The Africans get most of their animals by sneaking up behind them while they are not looking. But you could not do this with the pushmi-pullyu— because, no matter which way you came towards him, he was always facing you. And besides, only one half of him slept at a time. The other head was always awake—and watching. This was why they were never caught and never seen in Zoos. Though many of the greatest huntsmen and the cleverest menagerie-keepers spent years of their lives searching through the jungles in all weathers for pushmi-pullyus, not a single one had ever been caught. Even then, years ago, he was the only animal in the world that had two heads.

---

extinct—*none of its kind is living*

Well, the monkeys set out hunting for this
animal through the forest. After they had gone
a good many miles, one of them found peculiar
footprints near the edge of a river; they knew
that a pushmi-pullyu must be very near that
spot.

Then they went along the bank of the river
a little way and they saw a place where the grass
was high and thick; and they guessed that he
was in there.

So they all joined hands and made a great
circle around the high grass. The pushmi-pullyu
heard them coming; and he tried hard to break
through the ring of monkeys. But he couldn't
do it. When he saw that it was no use trying to
escape, he sat down and waited to see what they
wanted.

They asked him if he would go with Doctor
Dolittle and be put on show in the Land of the
White Men.

But he shook both his heads hard and said,
"Certainly not!"

They explained to him that he would not
be shut up in a menagerie but would just be
looked at. They told him that the Doctor was a
very kind man but hadn't any money; and people
would pay to see a two-headed animal and the

Doctor would get rich and could pay for the boat he had borrowed to come to Africa in.

But he answered, "No. You know how shy I am—I hate being stared at." And he almost began to cry.

Then, for three days they tried to persuade him.

And at the end of the third day he said he would come with them and see what kind of a man the Doctor was, first.

So the monkeys traveled back with the pushmi-pullyu. And when they came to where the Doctor's little house of grass was, they knocked on the door.

The duck, who was packing the trunk, said, "Come in!"

And Chee-Chee very proudly took the animal inside and showed him to the Doctor.

"What in the world is it?" asked John Dolittle, gazing at the strange creature.

"How does it make up its mind?" cried the duck.

"It doesn't look to me as though it had any," said Jip, the dog.

A New Pet for the Doctor

"This, Doctor," said Chee-Chee, "is a pushmi-

pullyu—the rarest animal of the African jungles, the only two-headed beast in the world. Take him home with you and your fortune's made. People will pay any money to see him."

"But I don't want any money," said the Doctor.

"Yes, you do," said Dab-Dab, the Duck. "Don't you remember how we had to pinch and scrape to pay the butcher's bill in Puddleby? And how are you going to get the sailor the new boat you spoke of—unless we have the money to buy it?"

"I was going to make him one," said the Doctor.

"Oh, do be sensible!" cried Dab-Dab. "Where would you get all the wood and the nails to make one with?—And besides, what are we going to live on? We shall be poorer than ever when we get back. Chee-Chee's perfectly right: take the funny-looking thing along, do!"

"Well, perhaps there is something in what you say," murmured the Doctor. "It certainly would make a nice new kind of pet. But does the er—what-do-you-call-it really want to go abroad?"

"Yes, I'll go," said the pushmi-pullyu, who saw at once, from the Doctor's face, that he was a man to be trusted. "You have been so kind to the animals here—and the monkeys tell me that I am the only one who will do. But you must promise me that if I do not like it in the Land of the White Men you will send me back."

"Why, certainly—of course, of course," said the Doctor.

"I notice," said the duck, "that you only talk with one of your mouths. Can't the other head talk as well?"

"Oh, yes," said the pushmi-pullyu. "But I keep the other mouth for eating—mostly. In that way I can talk while I am eating without being rude. Our people have always been very polite."

When the packing was finished and every-thing was ready to start, the monkeys gave a grand party for the Doctor, and all the animals of

---

go abroad—*go to a foreign country*

the jungle came. And they had pineapples and mangoes and honey and all sorts of good things to eat and drink.

After they had all finished eating, the Doctor got up and said,

"My friends: I am not clever at speaking long words after dinner, like some men; and I have just eaten many fruits and much honey. But I wish to tell you that I am very sad at leaving your beautiful country. Because I have things to do in the Land of the White Men, I must go. After I have gone, remember never to let the flies settle on your food before you eat it; and do not sleep on the ground when the rains are coming. I—er—er—I hope you will all live happily ever after."

When the Doctor stopped speaking and sat down, all the monkeys clapped their hands a long time and said to one another, "Let it be remembered always among our people that he sat and ate with us, here, under the trees. For surely he is the Greatest of Men!"

And the Grand Gorilla, who had the strength of seven horses in his hairy arms, rolled a great rock up to the head of the table and said,

"This stone for all time shall mark the spot."

---

mango—*a reddish, oblong tropical fruit*

And even to this day, in the heart of the jungle, that stone still is there. And monkey-mothers, passing through the forest with their families, still point down at it from the branches and whisper to their children, "Sh! There it is—look—where the Good White Man sat and ate food with us in the Year of the Great Sickness!"

Then, when the party was over, the Doctor and his pets started out to go back to the seashore. And all the monkeys went with him as far as the edge of their country, carrying his trunk and bags, to see him off.

Character Theme—Friendship, Gratitude, & Kindness

Thinking It Through

1. Why did Dr. Dolittle have to leave Africa and return home to Puddleby?

2. Why was a pushmi-pullyu such a rare animal?

3. What did Dr. Dolittle promise that the pushmi-pullyu could do if he did not like the new land?

4. What made the pushmi-pullyu decide to go with Dr. Dolittle?

The Kangarooster

His tail is remarkably long
And his legs are remarkably strong;
But the strength and the length of his legs
and his tail
Are as naught to the strength of his song.

He picks up his food with his bill;
He bounds over valley and hill;
But the height of his bounds can't compare
with the sounds
He lets out when he crows with a will.

—*Kenyon Cox*

naught—*nothing*

Wilbur Meets Charlotte

from *Charlotte's Web*
E. B. White

Wilbur the pig lives on the Zuckerman's farm
with the other animals and Lurvy, the farmhand.
But even with regular visits from the Zuckerman's niece Fern, Wilbur longs for a friend, until
one rainy day, he has an interesting surprise.

Loneliness

The next day was rainy and dark. Rain fell
on the roof of the barn and dripped steadily from
the eaves. Rain fell in the barnyard and ran in
crooked courses down into the lane where thistles
and pigweed grew. Rain spattered against Mrs.
Zuckerman's kitchen windows and came gushing
out of the downspouts. Rain fell on the backs of
the sheep as they grazed in the meadow. When
the sheep tired of standing in the rain, they
walked slowly up the lane and into the fold.

Rain upset Wilbur's plans. Wilbur had planned
to go out, this day, and dig a new hole in his yard.
He had other plans, too. His plans for the day
went something like this:

Breakfast at six-thirty. Skim milk, crusts,
middlings, bits of doughnuts, wheat cakes with

drops of maple syrup sticking to them, potato skins, leftover custard pudding with raisins, and bits of Shredded Wheat.

Breakfast would be finished at seven.

From seven to eight, Wilbur planned to have a talk with Templeton, the rat that lived under his trough. Talking with Templeton was not the most interesting occupation in the world but it was better than nothing.

From eight to nine, Wilbur planned to take a nap outdoors in the sun.

From nine to eleven he planned to dig a hole, or trench, and possibly find something good to eat buried in the dirt.

From eleven to twelve he planned to stand still and watch flies on the boards, watch bees in the clover, and watch swallows in the air.

Twelve o'clock—lunchtime. Middlings, warm water, apple parings, meat gravy, carrot scrapings, meat scraps, stale hominy, and the wrapper off a package of cheese. Lunch would be over at one.

From one to two, Wilbur planned to sleep.

From two to three, he planned to scratch itchy places by rubbing against the fence.

---

middlings—*ground wheat and bran*
trough—*long narrow feed box for animals*
hominy—*a type of corn*

From three to four, he planned to stand perfectly still and think of what it was like to be alive,
and to wait for Fern.

At four would come supper. Skim milk, provender, leftover sandwich from Lurvy's lunchbox,
prune skins, a morsel of this, a bit of that, fried
potatoes, marmalade drippings, a little more of
this, a little more of that, a piece of baked apple, a
scrap of upsidedown cake.

Wilbur had gone to sleep thinking about these
plans. He awoke at six and saw the rain, and it
seemed as though he couldn't bear it.

"I get everything all beautifully planned out
and it has to go and rain," he said.

For a while he stood gloomily indoors. Then
he walked to the door and looked out. Drops of
rain struck his face. His yard was cold and wet.
His trough had an inch of rainwater in it. Templeton was nowhere to be seen.

"Are you out there, Templeton?" called Wilbur.
There was no answer. Suddenly Wilbur felt lonely
and friendless.

"One day just like another," he groaned. "I'm
very young, I have no real friend here in the barn,
it's going to rain all morning and all afternoon,
and Fern won't come in such bad weather. Oh,

---

provender—*dry food such as hay for animals*

44

honestly!" And Wilbur was crying again, for the second time in two days.

At six-thirty Wilbur heard the banging of a pail. Lurvy was standing outside in the rain, stirring up breakfast.

"C'mon, pig!" said Lurvy.

Wilbur did not budge. Lurvy dumped the slops, scraped the pail, and walked away. He noticed that something was wrong with the pig.

Wilbur didn't want food, he wanted love. He wanted a friend—someone who would play with him. He mentioned this to the goose, who was sitting quietly in a corner of the sheepfold.

"Will you come over and play with me?" he asked.

"Sorry, sonny, sorry," said the goose. "I'm sitting-sitting on my eggs. Eight of them. Got to keep them toasty-oasty-oasty warm. I have to stay right here, I'm no flibberty-ibberty-gibbet. I do not play when there are eggs to hatch. I'm expecting goslings."

"Well, I didn't think you were expecting woodpeckers," said Wilbur, bitterly.

Wilbur next tried one of the lambs.

"Will you please play with me?" he asked.

"Certainly not," said the lamb. "In the first

gosling—*a young goose*

45

place, I cannot get into your pen, as I am not old enough to jump over the fence. In the second place, I am not interested in pigs. Pigs mean less than nothing to me."

"What do you mean, *less* than nothing?" replied Wilbur. "I don't think there is any such thing as *less* than nothing. Nothing is absolutely the limit of nothingness. It's the lowest you can go. It's the end of the line. How can something be less than nothing? If there were something that was less than nothing, then nothing would not be nothing, it would be something—even though it's just a very little bit of something. But if nothing is *nothing*, then nothing has nothing that is less than *it* is."

"Oh, be quiet!" said the lamb. "Go play by yourself! I don't play with pigs."

Sadly, Wilbur lay down and listened to the rain. Soon he saw the rat climbing down a slanting board that he used as a stairway.

"Will you play with me, Templeton?" asked Wilbur.

"Play?" said Templeton, twirling his whiskers. "Play? I hardly know the meaning of the word."

"Well," said Wilbur, "it means to have fun, to frolic, to run and skip and make merry."

"I never do those things if I can avoid them," replied the rat, sourly. "I prefer to spend my time eating, gnawing, spying, and hiding. I am a glutton but not a merry-maker. Right now I am on my way to your trough to eat your breakfast, since you haven't got sense enough to eat it yourself." And Templeton, the rat, crept stealthily along the wall and disappeared into a private tunnel that he had dug between the door and the trough in Wilbur's yard. Templeton was a crafty rat, and he had things pretty much his own way. The tunnel was an example of his skill and cunning. The tunnel enabled him to get from the barn to his hiding place under the pig trough without coming out into the open. He had tunnels and runways all over Mr. Zuckerman's farm and could get from

---

frolic—*to play*
glutton—*a person who eats too much*

stealthily—*done in a secret, cautious way*

one place to another without being seen. Usually he slept during the daytime and was abroad only after dark.

Wilbur watched him disappear into his tunnel. In a moment he saw the rat's sharp nose poke out from underneath the wooden trough. Cautiously Templeton pulled himself up over the edge of the trough. This was almost more than Wilbur could stand: on this dreary, rainy day to see his breakfast being eaten by somebody else. He knew Templeton was getting soaked, out there in the pouring rain, but even that didn't comfort him. Friendless, dejected, and hungry, he threw himself down in the manure and sobbed.

Late that afternoon, Lurvy went to Mr. Zuckerman. "I think there's something wrong with that pig of yours. He hasn't touched his food."

"Give him two spoonfuls of sulphur and a little molasses," said Mr. Zuckerman.

Wilbur couldn't believe what was happening to him when Lurvy caught him and forced the medicine down his throat. This was certainly the

dejected—*sad*

worst day of his life. He didn't know whether he could endure the awful loneliness any more.

Darkness settled over everything. Soon there were only shadows and the noises of the sheep chewing their cuds, and occasionally the rattle of a cow-chain up overhead. You can imagine Wilbur's surprise when, out of the darkness, came a small voice he had never heard before. It sounded rather thin, but pleasant. "Do you want a friend, Wilbur?" it said. "I'll be a friend to you. I've watched you all day and I like you."

"But I can't see you," said Wilbur, jumping to his feet. "Where are you? And *who* are you?"

"I'm right up here," said the voice. "Go to sleep. You'll see me in the morning."

Charlotte

The night seemed long. Wilbur's stomach was empty and his mind was full. And when your stomach is empty and your mind is full, it's always hard to sleep.

A dozen times during the night Wilbur woke and stared into the blackness, listening to the sounds and trying to figure out what time it was. A barn is never perfectly quiet. Even at midnight there is usually something stirring.

---

endure—*bear; put up with*

49

The first time he woke, he heard Templeton gnawing a hole in the grain bin. Templeton's teeth scraped loudly against the wood and made quite a racket. "That crazy rat!" thought Wilbur. "Why does he have to stay up all night, grinding his clashers and destroying people's property? Why can't he go to sleep, like any decent animal?"

The second time Wilbur woke, he heard the goose turning on her nest and chuckling to herself.

"What time is it?" whispered Wilbur to the goose.

"Probably-obably-obably about half-past eleven," said the goose. "Why aren't you asleep, Wilbur?"

"Too many things on my mind," said Wilbur.

"Well," said the goose, "that's not *my* trouble. I have nothing at all on my mind, but I've too many things under my behind. Have you ever tried to sleep while sitting on eight eggs?"

"No," replied Wilbur. "I suppose it *is* uncomfortable. How long does it take a goose egg to hatch?"

"Approximately-oximately thirty days, all told," answered the goose. "But I cheat a little. On warm afternoons, I just pull a little straw over the eggs and go out for a walk."

Wilbur yawned and went back to sleep. In his dreams he heard again the voice saying, "I'll be a friend to you. Go to sleep—you'll see me in the morning."

About half an hour before dawn, Wilbur woke and listened. The barn was still dark. The sheep lay motionless. Even the goose was quiet. Overhead, on the main floor, nothing stirred: the cows were resting, the horses dozed. Templeton had quit work and gone off somewhere on an errand. The only sound was a slight scraping noise from the rooftop, where the weather-vane swung back and forth. Wilbur loved the barn when it was like this—calm and quiet, waiting for light.

"Day is almost here," he thought.

Through a small window, a faint gleam appeared. One by one the stars went out. Wilbur could see the goose a few feet away. She sat with head tucked under a wing. Then he could see the sheep and the lambs. The sky lightened.

"Oh, beautiful day, it is here at last! Today I shall find my friend."

Wilbur looked everywhere. He searched his pen thoroughly. He examined the window ledge, stared up at the ceiling. But he saw nothing new. Finally he decided he would have to speak up. He hated to break the lovely stillness of dawn by using his voice, but he couldn't think of any other way to locate the mysterious new friend who was nowhere to be seen. So Wilbur cleared his throat.

"Attention, please!" he said in a loud, firm voice. "Will the party who addressed me at bedtime last night kindly make himself or herself known by giving an appropriate sign or signal!"

Wilbur paused and listened. All the other animals lifted their heads and stared at him. Wilbur blushed. But he was determined to get in touch with his unknown friend.

"Attention, please!" he said. "I will repeat the message. Will the party who addressed me at bedtime last night kindly speak up. Please tell me where you are, if you are my friend!"

The sheep looked at each other in disgust.

"Stop your nonsense, Wilbur!" said the oldest sheep. "If you have a new friend here, you are probably disturbing his rest; and the quickest way to spoil a friendship is to wake somebody up in the morning before he is ready. How can you be sure your friend is an early riser?"

"I beg everyone's pardon," whispered Wilbur. "I didn't mean to be objectionable."

He lay down meekly in the manure, facing the door. He did not know it, but his friend was

---

appropriate—*suitable*   meekly—*humbly and obediently*
objectionable—*disagreeable*

very near. And the old sheep was right—the friend was still asleep.

Soon Lurvy appeared with slops for breakfast. Wilbur rushed out, ate everything in a hurry, and licked the trough. The sheep moved off down the lane, the gander waddled along behind them, pulling grass. And then, just as Wilbur was settling down for his morning nap, he heard again the thin voice that had addressed him the night before.

"Salutations!" said the voice.

Wilbur jumped to his feet. "Salu-*what?*" he cried.

"Salutations!" repeated the voice.

"What are *they,* and where are *you?*" screamed Wilbur. "Please, *please,* tell me where you are. And what are salutations?"

"Salutations are greetings," said the voice. "When I say 'salutations,' it's just my fancy way of saying hello or good morning. Actually, it's a silly expression, and I am surprised that I used it at all. As for my whereabouts, that's easy. Look up here in the corner of the doorway! Here I am. Look, I'm waving!"

At last Wilbur saw the creature that had spoken to him in such a kindly way. Stretched across

---

gander—*a male goose*

the upper part of the doorway was a big spider-
web, and hanging from the top of the web, head
down, was a large grey spider. She was about
the size of a gumdrop. She had eight legs, and
she was waving one of them at Wilbur in friendly
greeting. "See me now?" she asked.

"Oh, yes indeed," said Wilbur. "Yes indeed!
How are you? Good morning! Salutations! Very
pleased to meet you. What is your name, please?
May I have your name?"

"My name," said the spider, "is Charlotte."

"Charlotte what?" asked Wilbur, eagerly.

"Charlotte A. Cavatica. But just call me Charlotte."

"I think you're beautiful," said Wilbur.

"Well, I *am* pretty," replied Charlotte. "There's no denying that. Almost all spiders are rather nice-looking. I'm not as flashy as some, but I'll do. I wish I could see you, Wilbur, as clearly as you can see me."

"Why can't you?" asked the pig. "I'm right here."

"Yes, but I'm near-sighted," replied Charlotte. "I've always been dreadfully near-sighted. It's good in some ways, not so good in others. Watch me wrap up this fly."

A fly that had been crawling along Wilbur's trough had flown up and blundered into the lower part of Charlotte's web and was tangled in the sticky threads. The fly was beating its wings furiously, trying to break loose and free itself.

"First," said Charlotte, "I dive at him." She plunged headfirst toward the fly. As she dropped, a tiny silken thread unwound from her rear end.

"Next, I wrap him up." She grabbed the fly, threw a few jets of silk around it, and rolled

Cavatica (kə·văt′ĭ·kə)
near-sighted—*able to see close things more clearly than distant things*

55

it over and over, wrapping it so that it couldn't move. Wilbur watched in horror. He could hardly believe what he was seeing, and although he detested flies, he was sorry for this one.

"There!" said Charlotte. "Now I knock him out, so he'll be more comfortable." She bit the fly. "He can't feel a thing now," she remarked. "He'll make a perfect breakfast for me."

"You mean you *eat* flies?" gasped Wilbur.

"Certainly. Flies, bugs, grasshoppers, choice beetles, moths, butterflies, tasty cockroaches, gnats, midges, daddy longlegs, centipedes, mosquitoes, crickets—anything that is careless enough to get caught in my web. I have to live, don't I?"

"Why, yes, of course," said Wilbur. "Do they taste good?"

"Delicious. Of course, I don't really eat them. I drink them—drink their blood. I love blood," said Charlotte, and her pleasant, thin voice grew even thinner and more pleasant.

"Don't say that!" groaned Wilbur. "Please don't say things like that!"

---

detest—*strongly dislike*

"Why not? It's true, and I have to say what is true. I am not entirely happy about my diet of flies and bugs, but it's the way I'm made. A spider has to pick up a living somehow or other, and I happen to be a trapper. I just naturally build a web and trap flies and other insects. My mother was a trapper before me. Her mother was a trapper before her. All our family have been trappers. Way back for thousands and thousands of years we spiders have been laying for flies and bugs."

"It's a miserable inheritance," said Wilbur, gloomily. He was sad because his new friend was so bloodthirsty.

"Yes, it is," agreed Charlotte. "But I can't help it. I don't know how the first spider in the early days of the world happened to think up this fancy idea of spinning a web, but she did, and it was clever of her, too. And since then, all of us spiders have had to work the same trick. It's not a bad pitch, on the whole."

"It's cruel," replied Wilbur, who did not intend to be argued out of his position.

"Well, *you* can't talk," said Charlotte. *"You* have your meals brought to you in a pail. Nobody feeds me. I have to get my own living. I

---

inheritance—*something passed from parents to children*

57

live by my wits. I have to be sharp and clever, lest I go hungry. I have to think things out, catch what I can, take what comes. And it just so happens, my friend, that what comes is flies and insects and bugs. And *further*more," said Charlotte, shaking one of her legs, "do you realize that if I didn't catch bugs and eat them, bugs would increase and multiply and get so numerous that they'd destroy the earth, wipe out everything?"

"Really?" said Wilbur. "I wouldn't want *that* to happen. Perhaps your web is a good thing after all."

The goose had been listening to this conversation and chuckling to herself. "There are a lot of things Wilbur doesn't know about life," she thought. "He's really a very innocent little pig. He doesn't even know what's going to happen to him around Christmastime; he has no idea that Mr. Zuckerman and Lurvy are plotting to kill him." And the goose raised herself a bit and poked her eggs a little further under her so that they would receive the full heat from her warm body and soft feathers.

Charlotte stood quietly over the fly, preparing to eat it. Wilbur lay down and closed his eyes. He was tired from his wakeful night and from the excitement of meeting someone for the first time. A breeze brought him the smell of clover—the sweet-smelling world beyond his fence. "Well," he thought, "I've got a new friend, all right. But what a gamble friendship is! Charlotte is fierce, brutal, scheming, bloodthirsty—everything I don't like. How can I learn to like her, even though she is pretty and, of course, clever?"

Wilbur was merely suffering the doubts and fears that often go with finding a new friend. In good time he was to discover that he was mistaken about Charlotte. Underneath her rather bold and cruel exterior, she had a kind heart, and she was to prove loyal and true to the very end.

---

brutal—*harsh; causing pain*
scheming—*tricky; deceitful*

Character Theme—Friendship

Thinking It Through

1. Why was Wilbur crying?
2. Why did Wilbur search his pen in the morning?
3. Why did Wilbur have such a hard time finding Charlotte? What kind of animal was she?
4. What did Wilbur discover about his new friend that made him wonder if he could ever be like her?

Farms

What jolly things are farms!
   They're many things in one—
I could not count their charms
   From now till set of sun.
They're lambs and sheep in pens,
   They're styes of pigs and sows,
They're yards of cocks and hens,
   They're byres of calves and cows,
They're fields of grass and corn,
   They're gardens with a wall
Where cabbages are born
   And beans and peas and all.

styes—*pigpens*
byre

They're dairies clean and cool,
    They're duck-ponds round and green,
They're sheds where every tool
    Of every sort is seen;
They're barns and harness-rooms
    Full of delightful smells,
They're borders full of blooms,
    They're ladders, pumps, and wells,
They're lofts of which one makes
    Great playrooms full of fun,
They're kitchens where the farmwife bakes
Her loaves and pies and little cakes
    And always gives you one.

—*Eleanor Farjeon*

61

A Dragon-fly

When the heat of the summer
Made drowsy the land,
A dragon-fly came
And sat on my hand,
With its blue jointed body,
And wings like spun glass,
It lit on my fingers
As though they were grass.

—*Eleanor Farjeon*

lit—*landed*

Captain Cook

from *Mr. Popper's Penguins*
Richard and Florence Atwater

Life changed for the Poppers when
Admiral Drake, the Antarctic explorer,
sent Mr. Popper a live penguin from
the South Pole.

"Call who Captain Cook?" asked Mrs. Popper,
who had come in so quietly that none of them
had heard her.

"Why, the penguin," said Mr. Popper. "I was
just saying," he went on, as Mrs. Popper sat down
suddenly on the floor to recover from her surprise, "that we'd name him after Captain Cook.
He was a famous English explorer who lived
about the time of the American Revolution. He
sailed all over where no one had ever been before.
He didn't actually get to the South Pole, of course,
but he made a lot of important scientific discover-
ies about the Antarctic regions. He was a brave
man and a kind leader. So I think Captain Cook
would be a very suitable name for our penguin
here."

"Well, I never!" said Mrs. Popper.

"*Gork!*" said Captain Cook, suddenly getting lively again. With a flap of his flippers he jumped from the tub to the washstand, and stood there for a minute surveying the floor. Then he jumped down, walked over to Mrs. Popper, and began to peck her ankle.

"Stop him, Papa!" screamed Mrs. Popper, retreating into the hallway with Captain Cook after her, and Mr. Popper and the children following. In the living room she paused. So did Captain Cook, for he was delighted with the room.

Now a penguin may look very strange in a living room, but a living room looks very strange to a penguin. Even Mrs. Popper had to smile as they watched Captain Cook, with the light of curiosity in his excited circular eyes, and his black tailcoat dragging pompously behind his little pinkish feet, strut from one upholstered

---

retreat—*to withdraw; go backward*
circular—*round*
pompously—*in a self-important manner*

upholstered—*covered with padding and material*

chair to another, pecking at each to see what it was made of. Then he turned suddenly and marched out to the kitchen.

"Maybe he's hungry," said Janie.

Captain Cook immediately marched up to the refrigerator.

"*Gork?*" he inquired, turning to slant his head wisely at Mrs. Popper, and looking at her pleadingly with his right eye.

"He certainly is cute," she said. "I guess I'll have to forgive him for biting my ankle. He probably only did it out of curiosity. Anyway, he's a nice clean-looking bird."

"*Ork?*" repeated the penguin, nibbling at the metal handle of the refrigerator door with his upstretched beak.

Mr. Popper opened the door for him, and Captain Cook stood very high and leaned his sleek black head back so that he could see inside. Now that Mr. Popper's work was over for the winter, the icebox was not quite so full as usual, but the penguin did not know that.

"What do you suppose he likes to eat?" asked Mrs. Popper.

"Let's see," said Mr. Popper, as he removed all the food and set it on the kitchen table. "Now

---

sleek—*smooth*

then, Captain Cook, take a look."

The penguin jumped up onto a chair and from there onto the edge of the table, flapping his flippers again to recover his balance. Then he walked solemnly around the table, and between the dishes of food, inspecting everything with the greatest interest, though he touched nothing. Finally he stood still, very erect, raised his beak to point at the ceiling, and made a loud, almost purring sound. *"O-r-r-r-h, o-r-r-r-h,"* he trilled.

"That's a penguin's way of saying how pleased it is," said Mr. Popper, who had read about it in his Antarctic books.

Apparently, however, what Captain Cook wanted to show was that he was pleased with their kindness, rather than with their food. For now, to their surprise, he jumped down and walked into the dining room.

---

solemnly—*seriously; gravely*

"I know," said Mr. Popper. "We ought to have some seafood for him, canned shrimps or something. Or maybe he isn't hungry yet. I've read that penguins can go for a month without food."

"Mamma! Papa!" called Bill. "Come see what Captain Cook has done."

Captain Cook had done it all right. He had discovered the bowl of goldfish on the dining-room window sill. By the time Mrs. Popper reached over to lift him away, he had already swallowed the last of the goldfish. "Bad, bad penguin!" reproved Mrs. Popper, glaring down at Captain Cook.

Captain Cook squatted guiltily on the carpet and tried to make himself look small.

"He knows he's done wrong," said Mr. Popper. "Isn't he smart?"

"Maybe we can train him," said Mrs. Popper. "Bad, naughty Captain," she said to the penguin in a loud voice. "Bad, to eat the goldfish." And she spanked him on his round black head.

Before she could do that again, Captain Cook hastily waddled out to the kitchen.

There the Poppers found him trying to hide in the still opened refrigerator. He was squatting under the ice-cube coils, under which he could barely squeeze, sitting down. His round, white-circled eyes looked out at them mysteriously from the dimness of the inside of the box.

"I think that's about the right temperature for him, at that," said Mr. Popper. "We could let him sleep there, at night."

"But where will I put the food?" asked Mrs. Popper.

"Oh, I guess we can get another icebox for the food," said Mr. Popper.

"Look," said Janie. "He's gone to sleep."

Mr. Popper turned the cold control switch to its coldest so that Captain Cook could sleep more comfortably. Then he left the door ajar so that the penguin would have plenty of fresh air to breathe.

"Tomorrow I will have the icebox service department send a man out to bore some holes in the door, for air," he said, "and then he can put a handle on the inside of the door so that Captain Cook can go in and out of his refrigerator, as he pleases."

"Well, dear me, I never thought we would have a penguin for a pet," said Mrs. Popper. "Still, he behaves pretty well, on the whole, and he is so nice and clean that perhaps he will be a good example to you and the children. And now,

---

ajar—*slightly open*   bore—*drill*

I declare, we must get busy. We haven't done anything but watch that bird. Papa, will you just help me to set the beans on the table, please?"

"Just a minute," answered Mr. Popper. "I just happened to think that Captain Cook will not feel right on the floor of that icebox. Penguins make their nests of pebbles and stones. So I will just take some ice cubes out of the tray and put them under him. That way he will be more comfortable."

The next day was quite eventful at 432 Proudfoot Avenue. First there was the service man and then the policeman and then the trouble about the license.

Captain Cook was in the children's room, watching Janie and Bill put together a jigsaw puzzle on the floor. He was very good about not disturbing the pieces after Bill had spanked him for eating one. He did not hear the refrigerator service man come to the back door.

Mrs. Popper had gone marketing for canned shrimps for the penguin, so that Mr. Popper was alone in the kitchen to explain to the service man what he wanted done to the refrigerator.

The service man put his tool bag down on the kitchen floor, looked at the refrigerator, and then at Mr. Popper, who, to tell the truth, had not shaved yet and was not very tidy.

"Mister," he said, "you don't need no ventilating holes in that there door."

"It's my icebox, and I want some holes bored in the door," said Mr. Popper.

They argued about it for quite a while. Mr. Popper knew that to get the service man to do what he wanted, all he had to do was to explain that he was going to keep a live penguin in the icebox, and that he wanted his pet to have plenty of fresh air, even though the door was closed all night. He felt a little stubborn about explaining, however. He didn't want to discuss Captain Cook with this unsympathetic service man, who was already staring at Mr. Popper as if he thought Mr. Popper was not quite right in his head.

"Come on, do what I said," said Mr. Popper. "I'm paying you for it."

"With what?" asked the service man.

Mr. Popper gave him a five-dollar bill. It made him a little sad to think how many beans it would have bought for Mrs. Popper and the children.

The service man examined the bill carefully, as if he didn't trust Mr. Popper too much. But at last he put it in his pocket, took a drill from his

---

ventilate—*to make openings for fresh air to get in and stale air to get out* tool bag, and made five small holes in a neat pattern on the refrigerator door.

"Now," said Mr. Popper, "don't get up. Wait a minute. There is one more thing."

"Now what?" said the service man. "I suppose now you want me to take the door off its hinges to let in a little more air. Or do you want me to make a radio set out of your icebox?"

"Don't get funny," said Mr. Popper indignantly. "That is no way to talk. Believe it or not, I know what I'm doing. I mean, having you do. I want you to fix an extra handle on the inside of that box so it can be opened from the inside of the box."

"That," said the service man, "is a fine idea. You want an extra handle on the inside. Sure, sure." He picked up his tool bag.

"Aren't you going to do it for me?" asked Mr. Popper.

"Oh, sure, sure," said the service man, edging toward the back door.

Mr. Popper saw that for all his words of agreement, the service man had no intention of putting on an inside handle.

"I thought you were a service man," he said.

"I am. That's the first sensible thing you've said yet."

---

intention—*a plan*

"You're a fine kind of service man if you don't even know how to put an extra handle on the inside of an icebox door."

"Oh, I don't, don't I? Don't think I don't know how. As far as that goes, I've even got a spare handle in my tool bag, and plenty of screws. You needn't think I don't know how to do it, if I wanted to."

Mr. Popper silently reached into his pocket and gave the service man his last five-dollar bill. He was pretty sure that Mrs. Popper would be annoyed at him for spending all that money, but it could not be helped.

"Mister," said the service man, "you win. I'll fix your extra handle. And while I am doing it, you sit down on that chair over there facing me, where I can keep an eye on you."

"Fair enough," said Mr. Popper, sitting down.

The service man was still on the floor, putting in the final screws that held the new handle in place, when the penguin came out to the kitchen on his silent pink feet.

Surprised at seeing a strange man sitting on the floor, Captain Cook quietly walked over and began to peck him curiously. But the service man was even more surprised than Captain Cook.

"*Ork,*" said the penguin. Or perhaps it was

the service man. Mr. Popper was not sure just
what had happened when he picked up himself
and his chair a moment later. There
had been a shower of flying tools, a
violent slamming of the door, and
the service man was
gone.

These sudden noises, of course,
brought the children running.
Mr. Popper showed them how the
refrigerator was now all remodeled
for the penguin. He showed Captain Cook, too,
by shutting him inside it. The penguin at once
noticed the shiny new inside handle and bit it
with his usual curiosity. The door opened, and
Captain Cook jumped out.

Mr. Popper promptly put Captain Cook back
inside and shut the door again, to be sure that the
penguin learned his lesson. Before long, Captain
Cook became quite skillful at getting out and was

ready to be taught how to get inside when the door was shut.

By the time the policeman came to the back door, Captain Cook was going in and out the refrigerator as easily as if he had lived in one all his life.

> You will enjoy reading the rest of the book, *Mr. Popper's Penguins,* to find out what happened when the policeman arrived and other adventures of the Poppers and Captain Cook.

Character Theme—Resourcefulness

Thinking It Through

1. Why did Mr. Popper name the penguin Captain Cook?

2. How did Captain Cook show that he was hungry and that he wanted seafood?

3. Why did the Poppers want holes drilled in their refrigerator?

4. What made Mrs. Popper accept Captain Cook as a pet?

Duck's Ditty

All along the backwater,
Through the rushes tall,
Ducks are a-dabbling,
Up tails all!

Ducks' tails, drakes' tails,
Yellow feet a-quiver,
Yellow bills all out of sight
Busy in the river!

Slushy green undergrowth
Where the roach swim—
Here we keep our larder
Cool and full and dim.

Everyone for what he likes!
We like to be
Heads down, tails up,
Dabbling free!

High in the blue above
Swifts whirl and call—
We are down a-dabbling
Up tails all!
—*Kenneth Grahame*

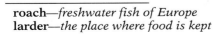

roach—*freshwater fish of Europe*
larder—*the place where food is kept*

Seal

See how he dives
From the rocks with a zoom!
See how he darts
Through his watery room
Past crabs and eels
And green seaweed,
Past fluffs of sandy
Minnow feed!
See how he swims
With a swerve and a twist,
A flip of the flipper,
A flick of the wrist!
Quicksilver-quick,
Softer than spray,
Down he plunges
And sweeps away;
Before you can think,
Before you can utter
Words like "Dill pickle"
Or "Apple butter,"
Back up he swims
Past Sting Ray and Shark,
Out with a zoom,
A whoop, a bark;
Before you can say
Whatever you wish,
He plops at your side
With a mouthful of fish!

—*William Jay Smith*

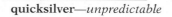

quicksilver—*unpredictable*

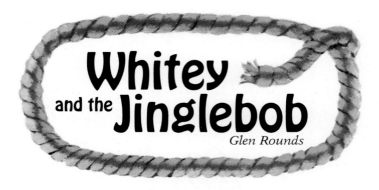

Whitey and the Jinglebob

Glen Rounds

At the time I speak of, Whitey was ten years old, or thereabouts. He had him a hand-me-down Stetson with a rattlesnake-skin hatband onto it, and a pair of Uncle Torwal's fancy stitched Fort Worth boots.

Jinglebob was about the same size and probably the same age. He got his name from the second-hand Stetson he wore. The brim of it had been tromped on by a horse at some time, so it sort of hung down on one side, the way a jinglebobbed calf's ear does. His father was a freighter. He had left the boy with Torwal and Whitey one trip, and Jinglebob'd just sort of stayed.

Torwal was an old-time cattle man, with legs that were bowed, a drooping red moustache, and a stiff arm from getting an Indian arrow in the early days.

These three lived by themselves, doing their own cooking, dish washing, and the like. They

---

Stetson—*a cowboy hat*
Torwal (tôr′väl)

freighter—*one who ships cargo*

ran the ranch with the help of a sooner dog,
name of Confusion.

This particular day, Torwal had gone to Lone
Tree to get the mail and some other odds and
ends. Whitey and Jinglebob were down in the
corral practicing up on their rodeo stuff. You
see, they were no great shakes for size, but none
the less they figured they were top hands, almost.
And it's a well-known fact that if you want to be a
top hand in any business, you have to practice.

So, when Torwal came back that afternoon,
he saw a considerable cloud of dust raising up
over the corral where he was keeping a bunch of
long yearlings and two-year-olds, fattening them
up for shipping. As he rode closer, he could hear
the excitement. He tied his horse and climbed up
on the fence to watch.

Jinglebob had just roped a big yearling and
got him snubbed up to the snubbing post in the
middle of the corral. He held him there while
Whitey put a rope around the critter and climbed
onto his back. Jinglebob turned his rope loose,
and the calf started an imitation of a Brahma bull
at the rodeo. Whitey rode about three jumps and
then was thrown. After he'd dusted himself off a

yearling—*an animal between one and two years old*
snub—*to stop a roped animal by turning its rope around a post*
Brahma bull—*a bull with a fleshy hump over its shoulders*

little, he roped another calf and Jinglebob tried to ride it.

Both boys were plastered with sweat and dirt. The calves likewise. Some were standing around with the tips of their tongues showing and foam on their chops.

"We're practicing to be top hands," Whitey told Uncle Torwal.

"Yessir!" said Jinglebob. "We're practicing on roping and bareback riding today."

"Fat stock like that gets hot mighty easy,"

stock—*cattle*

Torwal said, as they walked over to the windmill to get a drink.

"Yessir, it does for a fact," Whitey admitted.

"We'd sort of noticed that," said Jinglebob. "But if we are to be top hands, we have to keep in practice."

Uncle Torwal agreed that it was necessary for a top hand to keep in practice. But it occurred to him that such excitement wasn't exactly the best thing in the world for fattening calves.

Whitey and Jinglebob agreed that there was much in what he said. But how in the world were they to practice their riding, they wanted to know.

Uncle Torwal thought that over a while. Then he said, "It's too late to do anything about it today. But tomorrow, we'll build a contraption like one I saw down on the Reservation one time."

"I just don't see how we can learn to ride on a contraption," Whitey said. Jinglebob agreed with him.

"It'll give you a right brisk bit of practice, and not sweat the fat off the beef," Torwal assured him. From then on, he would tell no more about it.

They talked about the contraption while they peeled potatoes and sliced bacon for supper. Torwal listened to them as he mixed the biscuits, but wouldn't say anything. Even after they'd gone to

occur—*to have a sudden thought*

bed, Whitey and Jinglebob talked of what kind of contraption Uncle Torwal could be thinking of. But they could make nothing of it. So they finally took their Stetsons off and went to sleep.

The next morning, as soon as they'd had breakfast and cleaned up the kitchen, Torwal took them out behind the blacksmith shop. He started the boys digging four deep post holes, set in a square some ten feet across, while he fastened four rings onto the ends of an old oil drum with strap iron and rivets. They finished the holes about the time he was done with the drum.

Then, from the pole pile, Torwal picked out four long, stout ash poles. He helped the boys set these up in the post holes and tamp them solid, after he'd fastened a good length of rope to the top of each. When that was done, he fastened the ropes to the rings in the drum, so it hung on its side some four feet off the ground. After he'd taken an old saddle and strapped it on the drum, he stepped back and looked the thing over.

"There's your contraption," he said, looking right pleased with himself. Whitey and Jinglebob looked at the contraption and then at each other.

---

rivet—*a metal bolt or pin*
stout—*strong*

tamp—*to pound down by a series of taps or blows*

82

After a while, Whitey spoke up. "It looks like a kids' play-toy to me," he said, looking right unhappy.

"Yessir! That's just the way it looks to me," Jinglebob said. "It'd be fine for kids to play with. But I don't see what we can do with it."

"Mebbe you won't feel so disappointed about it when you've given it a whirl," said Torwal. "Supposing you try it out first, Jinglebob."

Jinglebob wasn't at all enthusiastic. But he didn't want to hurt Uncle Torwal's feelings after he'd gone to so much trouble building the thing. So he said it was all right with him. He and Whitey both figured Uncle Torwal must be slipping. As a general thing, he understood how they felt about having to fool with kid stuff.

They hated to think how cowboys roundabout would laugh if the word got around they played with such a sissy contraption! But for now, there was nothing they could do but make the best of it. So Jinglebob climbed into the saddle. He sat there looking sheepish while Uncle Torwal took up the stirrups to fit him.

"All set?" Torwal asked after a bit.

"Yessir, I reckon so," Jinglebob said, without much enthusiasm.

"Well, hang onto your hat!" And Torwal and

Whitey started shoving the limber poles one way and another.

That was when Jinglebob got the surprise of his life. With the drum swung from the tops of those limber poles whipping in all directions, it proved to be anything but a solid proposition. In less than no time at all, Jinglebob sailed off and rolled head over heels.

He was somewhat surprised. So was Whitey, for that matter. They looked at one another. They looked at the contraption. Uncle Torwal just looked pleased with himself. "Still think it's a kids' play-toy?" he asked after a while.

"No, sir! That thing bucks worse than Black Diamond at Cheyenne! But of course I wasn't expecting anything so brisk. If I could try it again, I don't reckon I'd have any trouble staying with it."

But the second try was no better than the first. Then Whitey tried it and was piled. After that, they talked Torwal into trying it, and were mighty pleased when he was thrown almost as quick as they had been. They all took turns from then on. With practice, they found that they could make the contraption do just about anything an outlaw horse could do, and a few that would be

---

limber—*easily bent; flexible*
outlaw horse—*a horse that is especially wild*

84

right difficult for the best horse that ever wore hair.

While they were still experimenting with the contraption, Smoky Tom Nelson rode up with one of his cowboys to see Torwal about something or other. They were right pleased to see Torwal playing with a kids' contraption, they said, with wide grins.

After some talk back and forth, Torwal invited them to try a ride themselves, provided it was all right with Whitey and Jinglebob.

"Yessir! We'd be right pleased to have you try out our play-toy!" they both said, grinning happily at the idea.

"You try it first, Texas," Smoky said to the cowboy with him.

This cowboy was from Texas, where they go in more for fancy trimmings than is usual in Lone Tree County. Even for a Texas man, he was a sight for sore eyes. His saddle was crusted almost solid, wherever he wasn't sitting on it, with silver conchas and doo-dads of all kinds. He had little looking glasses set into the corners of his saddle skirts, in addition to the silver. His stirrups were covered with long *tapaderos* that near touched the ground. His Stetson was so tall and so wide in the brim, and had so many silver conchas on it, that Whitey and Jinglebob figured he must need both hands to take it off. Altogether, he was so loaded down that it seemed a wonder his horse wasn't swaybacked.

"I'm a man that will ride anything that has four legs and hair on the outside," the Texas man said. "When I set onto an outlaw's back, it's as if

---

concha—*a shell-shaped decoration*
tapadero (tăp′ə·dā′rō)—*a leather hood for a stirrup*

I'd suddenly growed there. Many a killer hoss has taken one look at me walking up to him and re-formed on the spot, being from then on a perfect mount fer ladies and children. I've rode hosses that couldn't be rode, setting straight up, scratch-ing them fore and aft according to Association rules, meanwhile reading the latest copy of *Grit*. But that's no hoss. It's nothing but a kids' con-traption."

"Of course, if you're not feeling good . . ." Torwal began.

"I'm in fine fettle," the Texas man said. "Never felt better! Bright-eyed and bushy-tailed, that's me. But I still say that's a complete waste of time for a man of my talents!"

Whitey and Jinglebob were bug-eyed with ex-citement. They figured that if anybody could ride the contraption, it was the Texas man. A fellow that looked as grand and talked as fancy as that must be about the best in the country.

But the long and short of it was that after Torwal and Smoky talked the Texas man into try-ing just one ride, he did no better than anyone else. The first time the contraption flung him, he allowed it was an accident. He hadn't expected it to be so brisk, he said.

Grit—a newspaper   **in fine fettle**—*in good shape*

"Just what I said," Jinglebob whispered to Whitey.

But the second try was no better. The third was as bad. After that, he picked himself up and limped over to the contraption and looked it over close, while nobody said a word.

"Where in the world did you get this contraption? What do you use it for?"

"In this country we build such things for the children to learn to ride on," Torwal told him. "To sort of start them on something easy until they can handle a real horse."

The Texas man brushed dust off himself, then spoke up again. "Up to now I've rode everything that come down the pike," he said. "I've rode 'em saddled and I've rode 'em slick. I've rode big hosses down to nubbins and little hosses down to nuthin! And then I get flang by a kids' contraption! All I can say is, yuh should name it the Lone Tree Killer and enter it in the contest at Cheyenne this fall."

And from then on, the Lone Tree Killer's reputation spread. Any Saturday afternoon, you could find half the cowboys in Lone Tree County gathered around and waiting their turn to get thrown

---

nubbin—*anything small or undeveloped*

by it. Whitey and Jinglebob had to wait their turn at it like everyone else. They no longer felt it was a kids' contraption. And they had plenty of company when they practiced to be top hands.

Character Theme—Resourcefulness

Thinking It Through

1. Why were Whitey and Jinglebob roping and trying to ride Uncle Torwal's calves?

2. What did the boys think of Uncle Torwal's contraption when it was finished?

3. How did Smoky Tom Nelson and his Texas cowboy react when they saw Torwal taking his turn on the contraption?

4. Why were Whitey and Jinglebob excited about having the Texas cowboy try out their contraption?

5. What important lesson did the boys learn from Uncle Torwal's contraption?

Go West, Young Man

There was a wise fellow
  Who said, "It is best
For ambitious young folks
  To go West, West, West."

Out where the plains
  And the coyotes are,
The eye of a man
  Can see far, far, far.

Out where the mountains
  Stand bare of a tree,
The soul of a man
  Can feel free, free, free.

—Dorothy Hall

ambitious—*having the desire
  to achieve something*

The Cowboy's Life

The bawl of a steer,
To a cowboy's ear,
   Is music of sweetest strain;
And the yelping notes
Of the wild coyotes
   To him are a glad refrain.

For a kingly crown
In the noisy town
   His saddle he wouldn't change;
No life so free
As the life we see
   Way out on the Yaso range.

The rapid beat
Of his broncho's feet
   On the sod as he speeds along,
Keeps living time
To the ringing rhyme
   Of his rollicking cowboy song.

The winds may howl
And the thunder growl
   Or the breezes may safely moan;—
A cowboy's life
Is a royal life,
   His saddle his kingly throne.
           —*James Barton Adams*

---

broncho—*bronco, a wild horse or pony
  of the western plains*
rollicking—*lively and carefree*

91

Andy Stands Guard

Stanley Young

Twelve-year-old Andrew Jackson has been
left with his aunt to guard the house while his
mother and uncle go off looking for news of
Andy's brother Hugh, a soldier in America's
War for Independence.

Aunt Crawford and Andy
watched them wind their way down
the rough corduroy road. Then
they turned to go into the house.

"Your mother's a brave woman,"
Aunt Crawford said, wiping her eyes
on her apron.

Andy nodded. Secretly, he
didn't see why his mother had to
go looking for Hugh. Hugh was a
soldier, a man now. He could look
out for himself.

"Come now," Aunt Crawford
said. "We've the dishes to do."

A frown broke over Andy's
face. "Uncle said I was to guard the
house."

corduroy road—*a road made of logs laid crosswise,
giving it the texture of corduroy cloth*

"You can guard from the kitchen," Aunt Crawford said, smiling.

Andy took up his gun and reluctantly followed her. He dried the dishes faithfully, but down to the last pewter cup his eyes and mind were out of the window. He had set his gun up in one of the cabin rifle holes, ready for action. Every cabin, as well as every blockhouse, had these square openings about every five feet around the entire building. Andy kept darting from one hole to the other as if he expected a raid any minute. His jumping made his aunt nervous.

"You'll have me jumping next," she said. "Go on outside."

Andy grabbed up his rifle and tore for the door. There was a tall pine just outside. With his gun fastened to his belt with leather thongs, Andy shinnied up the pine, hugging the tree with his knees until his hands caught the first branch. He pulled himself up and climbed to the highest branch. Shading his eyes, he looked out over the landscape. Far below was Twelve Mile Creek, filled with logs pushing their slow way down the valley to the Catawba. Up the valley, right, he

---

pewter—*a silvery-gray metal made of tin and lead*
shinny—*to climb up a tree, pole, or rope by gripping it with both
    hands and feet*
Catawba (kə·tô'bə)—*a river in North and South Carolina*

could see the smoke curling from Long Potter's house.

Andy looked away to the left. As far as he could see, the landscape lay peaceful in the gray morning light. But when he looked nearer he saw something that almost made him fall out of the tree. Not a hundred yards away, in the edge of the forest, he saw a man dodging from right to left and back again. The man was evidently pursuing something, but Andy could not see what it was. The man wore buckskins like everyone else. But his face, at this distance, could not be recognized.

Behind the man, only a few steps now, Andy could see the copper-brown, half-naked figure of an Indian brave. The Indian was following the settler, step by step, and gaining on him. Andy saw the Indian raise his tomahawk high above his head. Almost instinctively, almost before he had time to be afraid, Andy pulled his rifle tight to his shoulder and fired.

The woods rang with the sound. Andy looked and saw that the Indian had disappeared and the white man was turning his head from side to side in surprise trying to locate the direction of the shot. Andy slid to the ground. He

instinctively—*done without stopping to think*

94

stopped long enough to ram fresh shot and pow-
der into his gun. Then he hurried toward the
spot where he had seen the Indian. Aunt Crawford came out of the house and called to him, but
he ran on.

The Schoolmaster

It took Andy no more than a minute to reach
the spot. When he saw the white man's long
black hair and his hawkish nose he recognized

him at once. Old Horn-Rim, the schoolmaster. Andy ran up to him, shouting.

"Why, Master Jackson!" the schoolmaster exclaimed. "Did you fire that shot just now?"

"I did, sir," Andy said.

"Well now, that's a pity. I was pursuing one of the various diurnal lepidopterous insects that so abound in this region—"

"And an Indian was after you," Andy said shortly. "I shot at him from that tree. He was about to tomahawk you."

The schoolmaster's eyes widened. Andy left him and ran over to the tree close by where he saw the bark scarred. His shot had hit the tree behind which the Indian had hidden.

"Here," Andy said. "Here are his footprints, right enough."

"Well," the schoolmaster said. "Well, I thought the Indians were peaceable around here."

"There's a war on," Andy said. "The Redcoats get them stirred up."

There was a pause. The schoolmaster smiled down at the excited boy.

"Andy, I suppose if there's one person

---

diurnal (dī·ûr′nəl)—*active in the daytime*
lepidopterous insects (lĕp·ĭ·dŏp′tər·əs)—*butterflies and moths*

around here whose life you shouldn't be too particular about, it's the schoolmaster's."

Andy looked embarrassed, not knowing what to say. Old Horn-Rim was all right, but he wasn't very exciting, as a rule.

"What did you say you were chasing?" Andy asked, anxious to change the subject. His eyes peered into the shadows of the forest.

"A butterfly," the schoolmaster said. "A very rare one." Wasn't that like Old Horn-Rim, Andy thought? Out chasing butterflies when there was a war going on! But the schoolmaster's next words changed Andy's opinion of him.

"Tomorrow I'm going East to fight. Colonel Davie is an old friend of mine," the schoolmaster said. "And the colonies need every last man of us," he added.

As if he had read Andy's thoughts, the schoolmaster took the rifle and tested it in his hands.

"Loaded?" he asked.

Andy nodded. The schoolmaster raised the gun to his shoulder.

"See that bare limb over there? That dead one on the poplar?" he asked.

Andy nodded again. Surely the schoolmaster wasn't going to try to hit that! It was too far.

When the schoolmaster fired, Andy saw the
branch on the poplar fall to the ground. He was
speechless. The schoolmaster handed the gun
back to Andy.

"Let's walk over to your house," he said. "I
want to tell your aunt that her brave nephew
saved my life."

Andy walked along with him in silence,
thinking. Old Horn-Rim, what a shot! Never
again would he judge anyone by his outward
appearance. And never again would he make
fun of the schoolmaster, or hide
hoptoads in the three-legged desk.
Andy decided that perhaps
his mother was
right in
wanting him
to be a school-
master. Or maybe
he would be a law-
yer, as Old Horn-
Rim had so often
suggested.
"If you'd
been where I was

you'd have hit that
Indian, certain," Andy said.

"I wouldn't have tried to hit him. I'd have
frightened him away, as you did, Andy," the schoolmaster replied.

Andy looked puzzled.

"The Indian is fighting for his land the same
way we're fighting the British. No wonder they
hate us, lad," the schoolmaster went on. "All the
decent settlers—your father, your uncle, and most
of them around here—bought their lands from the
Indians. A lot of others just grabbed theirs, at the
point of a rifle."

As the schoolmaster talked on, Andy forgot
to be sorry over missing the Indian. He was glad
now that he had only hit the tree. Maybe the Indians were like white men, some of them all right
and some not.

"You'll probably have to fight Indians the rest
of your life, if you choose to live in the wilderness," the schoolmaster said. "But don't just use
them for rifle practice."

Aunt Crawford was halfway to the forest when
Andy and the schoolmaster came out. Her eyes
were questioning and fearful well before she spoke.

Andy told her, simply, what had happened, and the schoolmaster offered to stay at the cabin until Mr. Crawford came home.

Andy protested against this. He assured his aunt that one man around the place was quite enough.

The schoolmaster smiled. "The Scotch-Irish are a stubborn lot," he said. "The salt of the earth, though. How do I know? I'm one myself."

And then shaking Andy's hand and thanking him again, elaborately and at length in three-syllable words, he started down the path toward Twelve Mile Creek. Andy looked after him and saw with amazement that the schoolmaster had begun to dodge back and forth, on and off the path, just as he had been doing when the Indian was after him.

"All that for a diurnal lepidopterous insect," Andy said.

Aunt Crawford stared at him with her eyes popping.

"What! Were you swearing, Andrew?" she asked severely.

"No'm," he said. "I was merely discussin' butterflies."

---

elaborately—*in great detail*

Aunt Crawford shrugged her shoulders and decided that the Indian affair had momentarily robbed her nephew of his wits. She turned and went into the house. Andy, his eyes on the forest, stood in silent watch by the door wondering what he would do if a Redcoat suddenly appeared over the hill.

Character Theme—Respect

Thinking It Through

1. Why did Aunt Crawford let Andy go outside?
2. How did Andy save the schoolmaster's life?
3. What did the schoolmaster do that amazed Andy?
4. What lesson did the schoolmaster teach Andy that day?

From the Bible

The Lord seeth not as man seeth; for man looketh on the outward appearance, but the Lord looketh on the heart.
—1 Samuel 16:7

Our Native Land

God bless our native land!
Firm may she ever stand,
　　Through storm and night:
When the wild tempests rave,
Ruler of wind and wave,
Do Thou our country save
　　By Thy great might!

For her our prayers shall rise
To God, above the skies;
　　On Him we wait:
Thou Who art ever nigh
Guarding with watchful eye,
To Thee aloud we cry,
"God save the State!"

—*C. T. Brooks*

---

native land—*homeland*　　　　**rave**—*roar*
tempests—*storms*

No
Other Land

There is no other land like thee,
No dearer shore.
Thou art the shelter of the free,
The home, the port of liberty,
Thou hast been, and shalt ever be,
Till time is o'er.

—*James Gates Percival*

Tall Bram of LITTLE Pigeon

Manly Wade Wellman

As you read this story, see
how long it takes you to figure
out who Tall Bram is.

The boy and man were finishing their half-camp. Real pioneer axmen on the Indiana Trace in the 1820s might have smiled at it—three rickety log walls, the south side open, the twig-thatched roof slanting and swaybacked. But it was the best the boy and man could do.

"Nevis," said Wilmore Cutler to his son, "You've done a man's work all day yesterday, and most of today." He peered through the trees to where water gleamed. "Rest now—ramble a little, but not far. We don't know our way even around this quarter-section of timber we're claiming on. I'll have some kind of supper at sundown."

"And tomorrow we'll finish the roof, Pa," said Nevis Cutler. He was not tall for his age, but wiry and square-faced. He smiled to cheer his father.

"And we've got all the rest of autumn to clear land for spring planting."

Stooping above the bundles that had been unloaded from the wagon, he searched out a book he loved to reread and headed for the creek. Nevis had heard the name of the creek—Little Pigeon. To him it looked almost as broad as a river, and it ran swift and deep here. Nearby was the start of a village called Gentryville. And through the woods were scattered other home-steads. Perhaps enough neighbors to help him and his father scare away wolves, bears, or In-dians. The new life might not be bad, if they learned to live it.

Sitting, he looked at the creek. It must have plenty of fish. The two Cutlers must consider every possible food supply to see them through the coming winter. He opened the book. Every time Nevis read it, he liked it better. Then, "Hey," grumbled somebody behind him.

He looked up. It was a boy a year older than himself, and probably twice as heavy. A scowling face, round and doughy as an uncooked pudding, slanted above him. Close-set eyes gleamed. The fat boy was looking hard for trouble. "What you doin' here?" demanded the grumbling voice.

---

homestead—*a place where a family makes its home*

"My father and I are proving up this claim," said Nevis.

"Ain't got no right here." The scowl deepened. "What's your name?"

"Nevis Cutler. And I do have a right here."

"You callin' me a liar?" A meaty hand clamped on Nevis's shoulder. The other hand grabbed his book. The fat boy snarled and tossed the volume toward some bushes.

But out of those bushes shot an arm longer and bonier than Nevis thought possible. Its big hand caught the book in midair. Then the owner of the arm strode into view, a towering buckskin figure only a little shorter than the creekside saplings.

"Turn him loose, Tady," said the tall one, and the fat hand dropped from Nevis's shoulder.

The newcomer was the same age as Nevis. His legs in their fringed buckskin were mostly gigantic shins, and the feet in the worn moccasins were immense. Big, too, was the hand that held the book, and big was the protruding Adam's apple on the lean corded neck, and extra big the jutting nose below the black brows.

"What you botherin' around for, Bram?" blustered Tady.

---

prove up—*to meet the requirements for receiving public land by living on the land for a specified period and improving it*

jutting—*sticking out; projecting*

"I don't like fights started by big fellers agin little 'uns," was the deep, quiet reply.

"Awwww!" Tady could find no more to say than that. He turned and trudged away, plainly afraid to look back. The tall boy in buckskin smiled down at Nevis. His smile relieved the ugliness of his face.

"This book," he said, gazing at its cover. *"Gulliver's Travels.* Never heard tell on it. Books ain't as frequent as wildcats here in Indiany. But," he went on with sudden earnestness, "readin's what I'd rather do than anything. My best friend's the feller who gits me a book I ain't read."

He opened the volume and stared at the page, his lips moving almost raptly. "Don't fret about Tady," he said after a moment, "Bad-talkin', but scared of anything more'n half his size. You named yourself to him. Nevis Cutler. Isn't your pa the new schoolmaster who allows to teach in Gentryville?"

"That's right," said Nevis. "We just came."

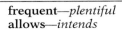

frequent—*plentiful*
allows—*intends*

"From where?" The tall boy dropped down and sat against a tree, his great knees cocking almost as high as his great nose.

"Pennsylvania. Pa was sick last year, lost his school. And my mother died, so we came here and made our claim. I heard Tady call your name—Bram, isn't it?"

Bram came unwillingly from his reading. "I'm glad about a school comin'. I'm too big to go—never had no more'n four months of school all told, but I allow to learn what I can by readin' and figgerin'. Nevis, I'm right sorry your ma died. Mine did, years back. I got a good stepma, though."

He offered the book, somewhat sadly. "Happen you'll lend me the book later, Nevis? I'll take right good care of it and give it back good as I got it. But now," and he rose, "This ain't what I come for. A pig of ours outstrayed. We fixed to butcher him for bacon, but a pen rail got loose—hog got loose too."

Nevis smiled, and Bram smiled back. "Ain't much of a joke, maybe, but somebody might like it. Anyway, if the pig's lost, my pa won't like it. I'm headin' down creek on his trail."

"I'll help you look," offered Nevis. "You can really see where the pig went?"

cocking—*rising up*

"There's his tracks. Look yonder, where he went to the edge of the creek. It shelves off right deep for a fair piece along here. And if he stops to eat acorns in that oak thicket yonder, maybe we kin—Whup!"

Bram had stopped so suddenly that Nevis, trotting behind, almost bumped his nose on the tall boy's sinewy back. "Somebody kind of told my pig howdy," he said, "and my pig never got the chance to say howdy back. Looky see yonder."

Nevis followed Bram's huge pointed finger. "Blood," he said. "Lots of it."

"A knife in the pig's neck," said Bram. "Then the feller dragged him along. Mark the tracks."

"An—Indian?" ventured Nevis.

"No. White man, and I know who. Only one feller 'round Gentryville parts wears boots with nails like that. Old Rube Demmin. He likes to get sidemeat and such things on the spot. I fear I've got to say something right unpleasant to him. If I don't hurry, he'll have the butchering done, and maybe half the eatin'."

Bram drew ahead, rounded a thicket, and for a moment was out of sight. When Nevis caught up again, Bram had stopped as before. He shot out an arm to stop Nevis beside him.

---

sinewy—*muscular*   venture—*to say or do even if it is a risk*

"Look," said Bram, and Nevis looked.

The two had come to a straggly line of bushes, against which lay a big fallen trunk. Beyond, the trees grew thinly, and from a jutting branch of a maple hung the carcass of a pig, smallish and limp. In the tree just beyond was another body, human, alive, and very much frightened. It was a middle-aged little man in rough homespun. Every bristle of unkempt hair and grizzled beard stood on end, and his eyes started from the pale face as they looked down to what had sent him climbing the tree.

"Overby's scrub bull," breathed Bram, as if he was trying not to laugh. "Overby's fence must have gone bad the same time ours did."

Nevis, staring, trembled. What Bram had called scrub bull seemed to him big and terrible. Its horns raked and prodded the bark of the tree, and the trunk, none too thick or strong, swayed and creaked. If Overby's bull looked big to Nevis, it must have looked monstrous to the man in the branches.

"Easy to see what happened," said Bram, smiling quietly. "Rube hung up my pig to bleed off. Bull smelled the blood and came ransackin'

---

grizzled—*gray, or streaked with gray*   unkempt—*messy* over to git mad—bulls do that. Rube was mad enough to yell or throw or whack at it—and it turned from the pig and ran him up a tree. He didn't have time to pick a good big 'un, even."

"But he's in danger," quavered Nevis. "That tree will break, or shake him out. Aren't we going to save him?"

"Certain sure. But I had to think a minute, and the minute's up." Turning, he bent his face toward Nevis, and the face was dead serious now. "Up a tree. That biggest 'un. I'll boost you."

A clutch, a heave, and Bram fairly hurled the smaller boy among the branches. So abrupt was Nevis's ascent that he dropped the Gulliver book. A moment later Bram had jumped over the big fallen log, slipped past the bushes, and was moving swiftly but watchfully toward the treed man and the shoving, pawing, raging bull.

By the time Nevis thought to wonder what Bram would do, Bram was doing it. He caught the bull's cocked-up tail in both his big hands, braced one boat-sized moccasin on the bull's hip, and threw his tall young strength into a fierce tug. The bull roared the way Nevis thought lions must roar, and Bram actually laughed, happy and

abrupt—*sudden; unexpected*   ascent—*a climb up*

fearless. Then, letting go, Bram whirled and ran. For all the scarecrow legs and big feet Nevis had thought clumsy, Bram could run like a deer. Over his shoulder he whooped, "Hi, bull! Hi, bull!"

The big spotted bulk whirled itself around, broad hoofs churning and splattering the loam and the fallen leaves. Down went its murderous head. It bounced after Bram with a deadly intentness.

Bram had reached another tree. He shot his hands up to the lower branches and swung up as nimbly as a dog-hunted racoon. A moment later the bull was raging, prodding, and pawing beneath him as it had raged, prodded, and pawed beneath Rube Demmin. But Bram laughed again, louder than the bull bellowed.

"I pick this to suit what I aim to do," he yelled across to Nevis. "This branch—"

The branch jutted straight out for many feet. Bram waited until the bull had paused beneath that very branch, shoving against the trunk as though it were a living enemy. Then Bram scrambled out along the branch until his weight forced its tip down, dropped lightly to the ground, and as before seized the bull's tail for a twist and a tug.

---

loam—*rich, dark soil*
intentness—*determination*

Bram supplemented this with a mighty kick at the bull's flank, and the bull turned in that direction.

Again Bram ran, and this time the bull did not need to be taunted into pursuit. It charged after its new and maddening foe. Bram headed for the tree where Nevis perched. Would he climb up? Nevis would welcome company. A chill that was not from the fall atmosphere made him shiver a bit.

Bram slid through the sparse bushes, then sprang high as a spy-hopping rabbit to clear the fallen log. Running on, he put himself behind a thick tree. The bull, blundering after him, drove into the log as Bram had foreseen and sprawled over it, flat and kicking.

supplement—*to add to*
taunted—*teased*
sparse—*thin; not many*

113

Once more Bram laughed.

"Hi, bull, git up! Here I am, over here! *Leave that book be!*"

Nevis had dropped the Gulliver book at the root of the tree into which Bram had boosted him. The bull, falling, had found its nose almost touching the strange little human-smelling object. Rising, the beast lowered its horns, poking and then tossing the book. Its pages fluttered as it flew through the air.

"Don't Bram, don't!" screamed Nevis from the branches, but Bram had sprung from his shelter. He rushed in, suddenly as fierce and angry as the bull itself. He stooped, caught up the *Gulliver.* For one sickened moment Nevis thought the bull had Bram. Not even the swift, long boy could slip aside from that rush.

Bram did not try to slip aside. He did the one thing in all the world he could and should do. Even as the

heavy head dipped to whip upward at him, he
planted one foot between the horns and hoisted
himself like a man climbing stairs. The bull
tossed, and Bram sailed like a leaf in a storm
above the bull's back, past its tail, down to earth.
He struck on one knee and got up running. The
bull was after him. They headed for the creek
and lost themselves among the trees. Then Nevis
heard Bram's loud yell and the splash of
something heavy falling into the
water.

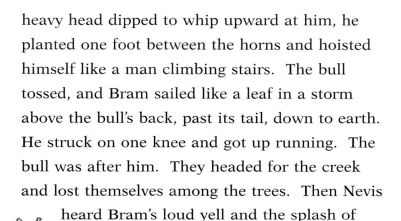

Silence. Nevis sat in
his tree, old Rube Dem-
min in his. A minute
crawled past. Another.
There was a rustle of
branches. Something
came slowly back into
view. Bram had the
Gulliver book open in
his big hands. His
feet moved

heavily and half gropingly, because his eyes were fixed on the print. He came to the tree where Nevis perched and set the big angle of an elbow against it. Lounging, he read on, grunting now and then in wonder and delight. Nevis climbed down and stood beside him, knees bobbing and swaying under him.

"Bram," he said, barely achieving a whisper.

"What's that?" Bram pried himself out of his wonderland of reading. "Well, Nevis, I got back your book. Couldn't let a scrub bull hook it to pieces."

"But the bull—"

"Him? He dogged me right to the bank of the Little Pigeon, where it was steepest and deepest. At the last moment I got time to jump sideways, and he kept goin' on. Did you hear him splash? That's how ten million bullfrogs must sound if they all hit the water at once. The current took him along, and it'll be a quarter-mile, near about, before he can find a low place to climb out. Let's go, because maybe he'll find his way back again."

He handed the book to Nevis, who wedged it into the waistband of his trousers. The two walked to where the bewhiskered Rube Demmin was lowering himself from his tree of refuge.

"Bram," the old man said shakily. "Bram, sakes alive! Ye saved my life, ye did."

"Oh, it wasn't nothin'," said Bram. " 'Scuse me, I didn't mean your life wasn't nothin'. I just mean I ain't had such fun since the Barker barn-raisin'. Next time a bull jumps you up, Mr. Demmin, you'll know how to handle him."

"Ye saved my life, boy," said Rube Demmin again. "To pay ye fer that, Bram, I'll give ye anythin'—anythin'—"

"A-well," said Bram slowly, "since you make that kind of fair offer, Mr. Demmin, will you give me the pig you stuck and hung up to butcher?"

"The pig?" said Rube Demmin, as if he had never heard of such a creature. Bram pointed helpfully, and Rube Demmin's whiskered face turned slowly gazing to where the carcass dangled. "Oh. That. Why, boy—" He turned back, but he did not look at Bram. "Take it. You're welcome."

"Thank you kindly," said Bram. The old man was walking away, somewhat as Tady had walked off earlier.

Bram chuckled.

"Ain't right to embarrass an old feller like that, Nevis. First off he seen the pig, he knew whose it was. But I'm saved the trouble of stickin' the pig—I don't like killin' things, even turkeys. Now to tote him home."

The way back was not far. Just beyond the Cutler homestead they came to Bram's cabin. It was well built, its log-ends notched and fitted with skill, the cracks well chinked and plastered with clay. The roof was of hand-split shakes, and Nevis judged that there was a loft above—elegance in that land and year.

"Yonder comes my pa," said Bram, lowering his end of the pig-laden pole. "I'll make you acquainted with him. He'll want to cut you off a hunk of the pig for helpin' me bring it back."

"That would be kind," replied Nevis. "And, Bram, I want to give you something, seeing how much you like it. You'd even fight a bull to save it, so you can have it."

From his waistband he drew the book about Gulliver and held it out.

"You mean that, Nevis?" Bram snatched the book as though he feared Nevis would change his mind. "Come up to the cabin right now. We've got ink in a jug—a little—and I'll cut us a quill pen. Then you can write in the front that it's my gift from you."

"That's right. From Nevis Cutler to his friend Bram—what's your full name, Bram?"

"Since we're goin' to be friends and neighbors," said the tall boy, "let's not have so much Bram. Folks that don't know me well, nor like me too much—like Rube Demmin and Tady—shorten my name down to Bram, because I was christened Abraham. But Ma and Pa and my friends call me Abe. Abe Lincoln. I'm proud to have you for a friend, Nevis Cutler."

"And," replied Nevis, "anybody'd be proud to have you for a friend, Abe Lincoln."

The boys shook hands.

Character Theme—Courage, Friendship, & Resourcefulness

Thinking It Through

1. Name the three boys in this story. Which one was a bully, and which one showed that he was already Nevis's friend?
2. How did Bram outsmart the bull that had "treed" Rube Demmin?
3. Do you think Mr. Demmin knew the pig belonged to Bram and his family? Why?
4. What was Bram's full name?

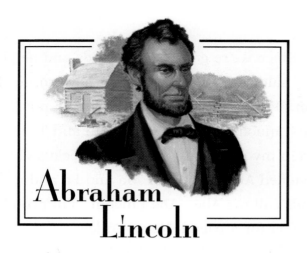

Abraham Lincoln

Remember he was poor and country-bred;
    His face was lined; he walked with awkward gait.
Smart people laughed at him sometimes and said,
    "How can so very plain a man be great?"

Remember he was humble, used to toil.
    Strong arms he had to build a shack, a fence,
Long legs to tramp the woods, to plow the soil,
    A head chuck full of backwoods common sense.

Remember all he ever had he earned.
    He walked in time through stately White House
           doors;
But all he knew of men and life he learned
    In little backwoods cabins, country stores.

Remember that his eyes could light with fun;
    That wisdom, courage, set his name apart;
But when the rest is duly said and done,
    Remember that men loved him for his heart.

                      —*Mildred Plew Meigs*

---

gait—*a particular way to move the foot*
duly—*at the proper time*

Dan Drake's First Patient

Marion Renick/Margaret C. Tyler

"This is the place," Dan Drake said to his
father. He pointed to the sign on the wide white
front door: *Doctor Wm. Goforth.* As the boy
reached up to bang the big brass knocker he told
himself that he, too, would someday have a similar sign on his door. For Dan had wanted to be a
doctor ever since he could remember. Now here
he was with his father, calling upon Dr. Goforth,
of Cincinnati, one of the few doctors in Ohio in
that year of 1799.

Dan turned once more to his father with the
question he had asked a dozen times as they had
made the trip from their home across the Ohio
River in Kentucky. "Do you think Dr. Goforth will
let me stay and learn about medicine from him?"

Before Mr. Drake could reply, the door was
opened by a sweet-faced woman who said she was
Mrs. Goforth. A few minutes later, Dan was ask-
ing his question of the doctor himself.

At first the boy had high hopes. For Dr. Goforth looked at him with interest and said there
was a great need for good doctors in Cincinnati,

Wm.—*an abbreviation for William*

and indeed in all the Ohio country. But then the physician asked about Dan's schooling. He shook his head as if displeased with Mr. Drake's explanation that Dan had never been to school because there was no school near enough for him to attend.

"But I can read!" Dan hastened to put in. "Mother taught me. I've read all the books we have at home. The Bible, the hymn book, the almanac, and *Aesop's Fables*, and Montellion's *History of Romance and Chivalry*."

Dr. Goforth looked at Dan as if he were going to shake his head again. But the look of longing on the boy's face must have made him change his mind. Then Dan said with all his heart in his voice, "I'd study very hard, sir, if you will only accept me as an apprentice."

So the doctor smiled and clapped Dan on the shoulder, promising to give him a trial. "But your life as a frontier doctor will be a hard one," he warned. "You'll have long, cold, lonely trips to make on winter nights. Wolves and wildcats will be your only company as you ride through trackless forests to attend the sick and dying in the cabins of the pioneers."

"I won't mind, sir, I'm *sure*," was Dan's answer.

"Your earnings will be uncertain," the doctor went on. "And when you do get paid it's likely to be in the shape of a fat hen or a bushel of corn. You'll make many a call miles off in the wilderness. And you'll get a dozen eggs for your pay. Often you won't even take the eggs because the sick person needs them worse than you do."

Dan was grinning now. "You can't scare me off, Dr. Goforth."

"Good lad!" The doctor nodded as if well satisfied. He turned to Mr. Drake to ask, "When can he start?"

"Can't I start now, Father?" Dan spoke as if he couldn't bear to wait a minute longer to enter the thrilling world of medicine.

And a truly thrilling world it was, he soon found. In the weeks that followed, Dr. Goforth gave him medical books to read and even began showing him how to prepare medicines.

In those days, there wasn't a drugstore full of pills on every other corner. A doctor had to make his own medicines from healing herbs, the bark of certain trees, and a few drugs brought by sailing vessels from countries across the sea. Dan soon learned how to stir up cough syrup or shake together a compound that was good for stomach pains. His steady, nimble fingers grew skillful

---

herbs (ûrbz)—*plants used as medicines*
compound—*something made by mixing two or more things*

at folding tiny squares of paper and filling them
with quinine to cure a fever. He liked this work.
It made him feel he was helping the doctor save
lives. Many times he saw his medicines in use as
he went along with Dr. Goforth to visit the sick.
Every evening, he wrote down in a notebook the
things he had learned on these visits.

quinine—*a substance taken from a bark
and used for treating malaria*

Dan began to dream of the time when he, too, would be allowed to treat the sick. He often imagined how he would doctor his first patient. He wondered if this patient would live in town or in some pioneer's cabin far out in the wilderness. For Dan soon had learned that Dr. Goforth's patients were not all within easy reach. Many of them lived miles away in the Ohio hills. Sometimes at night, Dan would hear the big brass knocker on the front door go *thump-thump-thump*. He would hurry downstairs to find a frightened father or husband who had ridden far and fast to fetch the doctor. Then Dan would hurry to the barn to saddle the doctor's horse, Copper. Quickly he would pack the saddlebags with medicines, bandages, and instruments. Dr. Goforth would gallop off into the darkness with the frightened man hurrying ahead of him.

One night Thad Harper rode in from his father's farm ten miles out of town. The whole family was down with swamp fever, Thad said, just as his knees gave way and he collapsed with the sickness on the doorstep. Dan helped the doctor get the young fellow into bed. Then the doctor looked thoughtfully at his apprentice.

---

swamp fever—*malaria, a disease transmitted by mosquito bites*

"I hesitate to ask this of you, Dan," he said. "But do you think you could take some medicine out to the Harpers? I'd go myself, but there is too much serious illness here in town just now. I don't dare leave."

"Of course, I can deliver the medicine!" Dan felt very sure of himself. "I'll saddle Copper and leave right away."

"I wish you could wait till morning," the doctor said. "But they need the medicine as soon as possible. And they'll worry about Thad, when he doesn't come home. Be sure to tell them he'll be all right in a few days. I'll give him some of the medicine I'm sending the rest of the family."

Dan took the packet the doctor handed him. He listened carefully to the instructions. "Make a good strong tea of this. Have each patient drink a cupful, then go to bed and keep warm. You are to observe how the patients are breathing, if their fever is high, if the palms of their hands are hot and dry. You can do that, can't you?"

"Of course, sir. I'll bring back a report to you," Dan promised. He dashed out to saddle Copper. He was going to treat his first patient!

The night was freezing cold but Dan didn't notice. His heart sang with the steady ca-LOP, ca-LOP, ca-LOP, ca-LOP of Copper's hooves on the frozen road. Then he felt Copper slow down. The horse stopped. It gave a gasp and a low moan. Dan was on the ground now, patting the horse's neck. "Nothing's the matter with you, Copper," he said in a soothing voice. "You're all right. Come now. Let's—"

But something *was* the matter. Copper's dark red body was swelling right before Dan's eyes. As fast as he could, he loosened the saddle, tearing at it with his cold, stiff fingers. By the time he got the saddle off, the horse's body had swollen until it looked like a huge barrel on four thin sticks of legs. Dan watched those legs anxiously. He was afraid they might double up. He knew if Copper once got down on the cold road, that might be the end.

Dan was almost sure he knew what was wrong. Copper probably had eaten too many oats for supper. Or had drunk too much water. And then Dan had galloped the horse too hard right after it had eaten. So now Copper had the heaves.

With every painful breath Copper drew, Dan grew more frightened. He tried to remember his notebook full of medical learning. When one of Dr. Goforth's human patients swelled up with indigestion, what had the doctor prescribed? Heat, Dan remembered. He shivered as he looked at the icy darkness around him. No heat there! Then he thought of the blanket under the saddle. He spread that over the horse. He took off his own coat and flung that, too, on Copper's back.

"The next thing to do is keep moving," he said aloud. "Come on, Copper. Come on. Just walk along easy-like. I'm right here beside you. Come on. Come on. That's the way, Copper. Keep moving. Keep going."

Step by step the shivering boy and the gasping horse went down the road. The sun was up by the time they came to a farmhouse. Dan was happy to see a large shed in the rear. He stopped and asked the farmer for permission to leave Copper there until he returned. He also explained his errand and asked how far it was to the Harper farm.

"About five miles," said the farmer's wife. "And you'd better have a bite to eat and warm yourself before you start out." She put an extra plate on the table for Dan. As they were eating breakfast, Dan told the farmer and his wife about his dream of becoming a doctor. He ended by saying the Harpers would be his first patients.

The farmer laughed. "You're wrong there," he said with a twinkle in his eyes. "You've already treated your first patient—and it was a horse."

For a moment Dan felt disappointed. Then he began to laugh, too. With a merry heart he set out on foot for the Harpers. He delivered the medicine, made a report for Dr. Goforth, and walked back to the farmer's shed for Copper. The horse was now much better. Dan thought he could safely ride the rest of the way home if he went slowly.

As Copper plodded along, Dan began to realize that the short winter day was almost ended. He should have been home long ago. Surely Dr. Goforth would wonder what had happened. So, the minute he finished making Copper comfortable in the barn, Dan ran to the house. As the door slammed behind him he heard Mrs. Goforth call to her husband, "Oh, Will! Here's Dan!" And both she and the doctor hurried to greet him.

"I'm sorry I was so long," Dan started to say. "I couldn't—"

"Never mind that," the doctor exclaimed. "You're safe, lad! That's all that matters. We feared you might have fallen into a ditch with Copper on top of you."

"It was Copper, sir—" Dan began again.

"Poor lad, you look frozen," Mrs. Goforth interrupted. "Here, let me help you off with your boots. And I'll make you a cup of hot tea."

At last Dan was allowed to tell what had happened. The doctor beamed with satisfaction at his account of how he had taken care of Copper. Later, after he had gone to the barn to have a look at his horse, he said, "Well, Dan, your first patient is getting along fine. You have the makings of a real doctor, my lad."

Four years later, Dan began to really practice medicine as a junior partner to Dr. Goforth. He had been well-trained by the older doctor. In his education, practical experience had taken the place of study in a college or a hospital, so Daniel Drake was given a diploma in medicine. It was the first doctor's diploma ever given west of the Allegheny Mountains. It said:

---

account—*retelling of events that took place*   Allegheny (ăl′ĭ·gā′nē)

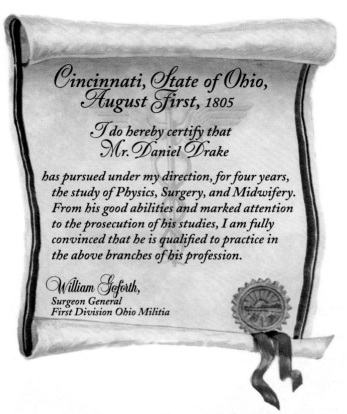

Cincinnati, State of Ohio,
August First, 1805

I do hereby certify that
Mr. Daniel Drake

has pursued under my direction, for four years,
the study of Physics, Surgery, and Midwifery.
From his good abilities and marked attention
to the prosecution of his studies, I am fully
convinced that he is qualified to practice in
the above branches of his profession.

William Goforth,
Surgeon General
First Division Ohio Militia

Character Theme—Industry & Service

Thinking It Through

1. What was Dan Drake's big dream?
2. Why had he never been to school?
3. Who was Dan's first patient?
4. How did Dan show that he would make a good doctor?

Yukon Trail

Willis Lindquist

When Steve got off the train in Nenana, Alaska, he had no idea that he would soon be driving a dog team over a dangerous wilderness trail to Canada's Yukon Territory. Could he pass the test and have a real home at last?

Under the lowering Alaskan sky young Steve Woodford stepped from the train at the snow-covered outpost of Nenana. He looked anxiously around for his Uncle Jim, the famous "Flying Doctor" of the Yukon of whom he had boasted so much at the orphanage.

For years he had dreamed of going to the Yukon. Now he was on his way and he was happy. He was going to have a real home and belong to a family. He hoped Uncle Jim and Aunt Bess would like him.

The young Indian who came up grinning couldn't have been over sixteen. "You're Steve?" he asked in perfect English. "Well, I'm Sam Ketchum. I've got a letter for you. There's been a lot of sickness up in the Yukon, and your uncle couldn't fly down for you."

Steve's heart sank as he took the letter. It was short. Uncle Jim wrote about how busy he was and that he might not be able to fly down for two or three weeks.

"Sam Ketchum is a young Indian guide who works for me," the letter went on. "I've told him to make you comfortable at the hotel. In a day or two he will be starting back for the Yukon with my new dog team. You could go with him if you wish,

lowering (lou′ər·ĭng)—*appearing dark and threatening*

133

but I would not advise you to do so. It is a 350-mile mush through wilderness and tundra, and it would be a hardship for a boy accustomed to the soft life of civilization."

Steve read the letter several times at the hotel. It disturbed him that his uncle should think he was soft.

When he joined Sam for a dinner of venison roast, he said, "I wanted to come up here last year, Sam. But Uncle Jim wouldn't let me. He wrote that I was too young. He said that the Yukon was a man's country and it was no place for a boy. So he made me wait a year. And now he thinks I'm soft. I'm going to show him, Sam. I'm going with you and the dog team."

Sam laughed. "It won't be easy," he warned. "But you have to learn about dogs sometime if you're going to be of any help to your uncle. We'll start at dawn."

It frightened Steve to think of the trip when he went to bed. He had never seen the big sled dogs. Some were part wolf and said to be dangerous.

It was still dark when the hotel man came with a set of fur breeches and a hooded parka, fur boots, and a fur sleeping bag.

---

mush—*a command to make sled dogs start or go faster; a journey by foot over snow with a dog sled*
parka—*a heavy winter coat with a hood*

Sam was waiting for him at the sled, with eleven mighty Eskimo dogs at their harnesses, anxious to be off.

"Better meet some of your dogs," Sam said. "This first one, your leader, is Mutt. He's been to the Yukon before, and he knows the trail."

The tawny big brute lowered its head and watched Steve with suspicion. Steve fought down his fear and leaned over to pet the dog. Its fangs bared in a snarl.

"Not too close," Sam warned. "Mutt doesn't know you yet. And you better stay clear of Kooga— this big malemute. He's a real troublemaker."

"Why is the sled tied to a tree?" Steve asked.

"Because otherwise they'd be off like a flash and we couldn't stop them," Sam explained. He pointed to an iron rod suspended above the ground at the rear of the sled. It looked like a narrow rake. "That's your brake. You step on it and the prongs dig into the snow and stop the sled."

They packed, and Steve got on top of the sled.

"Hold on!" Sam warned as he untied the rope from the tree.

The dogs were off, eleven big brutes harnessed in pairs except for Mutt, who took the lead.

---

tawny—*brownish-yellow; tan*
malemute (măl′ə·mūt′)—*husky; two breeds of Eskimo dog*

They raced over the snow in full gallop. The sled bounced and flew, and it took all of Steve's strength to hold on.

Standing on the runners in back, Sam gave a hearty laugh. "Dogs are always wild to get started. They'll soon slow down."

They did. For hours they went, skirting great slopes of spruce and Norway pine, and on and on into the still, white wilderness.

At midday they stopped for a few minutes' rest and a bite to eat.

"Now you drive," suggested Sam. "I'll run behind you for a while to get warm. But whatever you do, don't fall off the sled. You'll not be able to stop the dogs, and you'll lose them and the sled and all your food. It's not a good way to die."

Steve leaped on the runners. "Get going!" he shouted. Mutt turned his head back and looked at him, but nothing happened.

"Holler *mush*," Sam suggested. "When you want to go right, holler *gee*, and for left, *up*. And swing the sled around corners so it doesn't tip."

Steve nodded. "Mush!" he screamed. It worked. He stood proudly on the runners. He was driving a dog team!

There was real work to it, he soon discovered. Keeping the sled upright at curves was tricky, and he had to be careful to avoid the stumps and rocks that might smash the sled. On the down slopes he stood on the brake to keep from running over the dogs.

But suddenly it happened. He made the mistake of looking back too long at Sam who was jogging half a mile behind

them. He hit a slope, and his feet slipped from the runners. But he held on, dragging as the sled gathered speed downhill until it pushed the dogs forward into a wild, scrambled heap. Then the sled tipped.

It started one of the wildest dog fights Steve had ever seen. Each seemed to be blaming the others for what had happened, and they snarled and slashed with white fanged fury.

"Stop them! Stop them!" yelled Sam.

Steve stood frozen with fear. He didn't move. He didn't dare venture close.

Sam came up at full speed, screaming at the dogs. He pried them loose one by one with a snowshoe, and straightened their harnesses, which had become badly tangled. Then he mopped the sweat from his face.

"You'll have to learn how to do that quick," he gasped. "If you don't, you'll lose a dog or two before you know it."

For five days they went on, and then Sam began to have chills and fever. "I was in the hospital for a week before you came," he explained. "Maybe I left too soon. It's coming back."

By noon he was groaning with pain and could not leave the sled. "There's a settlement

venture—*to do or go at some risk*

over on Carlson Creek," he whispered. "You'd better get me there fast."

Steve reached the hollow among the bluffs in three hours, and only the women and children were there to meet them. The men were out on a week-long hunt.

"This one needs a doctor," said an old woman.

Steve went cold with dread, but he knew what had to be done. "Sam says my lead dog knows the trail well. I'll go get the doctor."

Sam mumbled in protest. "You'll stay here," he gasped. "Your uncle flies to this settlement every so often for a check."

"It might be weeks," said the old woman, "there is much sickness."

"I'll go," said Steve. He had no choice. Soon he found himself alone on the trail with a fierce pack of malemutes and Eskimo huskies, and he felt panic rising within him. He began to wonder if he could handle the team.

He began talking to the dogs, calling them by name as Sam had told him to do. He stopped for the night under a sheltering cliff near a staggering thicket of birches. Now the moment he dreaded most had come. He had to handle the big dogs.

---

bluffs—*high, steep banks or cliffs*

Steve tried not to show his fear. The big leader dog watched with yellow eyes as he approached, its ears flattened to the massive head. As Steve reached down to unfasten the harness, the wolf dog snarled.

"Easy, Mutt!" Swiftly, Steve unharnessed the dog and led it to the nearest birch tree and tied it up. He came away weak but bursting with happiness he had never known. *He could do it!* The other dogs, even the big malemute Kooga, were easy after that.

One day followed another with perfect weather. The dogs were beginning to know him; some even licked his hand. But Mutt, the leader, remained sullen.

Then he saw the plane in the sky one morning. It circled above him, his uncle waved, and Steve, forming big letters in the snow, told him to go to Sam at Carlson's Settlement.

A howling Arctic blizzard started that night and kept him in his sleeping bag for two days. The third morning dawned clear, and he looked out on a white world.

As they mushed north that afternoon, he became careless. He did not see the low branch until it struck him with a stunning blow in the face.

---

massive—*huge*　　　　　sullen—*unfriendly and resentful*

He was falling. "Don't lose your sled or you die!" Sam's words came roaring back to his ears.

With all his strength he tried to hold on. But it was no use. His fingers slipped, and he lunged headlong into the snow. He floundered. He tried to rise to his feet, but the earth seemed to tilt on end, and he couldn't tell which side was up.

The dogs and the sled were speeding away. He could see them vaguely. In a few moments they would be gone. There was nothing he could do to stop them. His food, his sleeping bag, even his snowshoes were on the sled. A man couldn't live very long on the lonely white tundra without them.

In that reeling instant of terror he seemed doomed. His minded cleared a little, and instinctively he cried out at the top of his lungs.

"Gee! Gee! Gee, Mutt."

He held his breath. For a terrible instant nothing happened. But suddenly the big lead dog swung to the right. He waited until the whole team had turned. Then he screamed again. "Gee! Gee, Mutt!" Once more the lead dog turned.

They were coming back now. Steve got to his feet and stumbled to meet them, waving his

---

vaguely—*hazily, not clearly*   tundra—*the vast, treeless plains of the Arctic area*

arms. He tripped over a snowdrift and sprawled before the onrushing team. That was all he could remember for a long time.

When he opened his eyes finally it seemed that a miracle had happened. Mutt, towering over him, was licking his face.

He threw his arms around the big dog, buried his face in the heavy fur, and let the tears come. Even a man could cry in Alaska, if there was no one to see his tears.

From that day on his uncle paid daily visits to watch his progress and to drop sandwiches and food from Aunt Bess. In the first of these packages he found a note.

"I have seen Sam," wrote his uncle. "He's doing fine, thanks to you. If you keep up your good speed, you should reach home in three days. We'll be waiting."

Steve felt a deep inner excitement. Home! In three days! He could drive a dog team now, and he felt sure that he could be of real use to his uncle. They would not find him soft and useless. They would like him.

Near sunset, three days later, as he came down the slope into the small settlement of Unison in the Yukon, his uncle and half the village came out to meet him. They were cheering and waving and smiling. His tall uncle wore a large smile and threw an arm over his shoulder.

"Good boy, Steve," he said warmly. To the people of the village he said, raising his voice, "I'm mighty proud to introduce you to my nephew Steve. He mushed all the way from Nenana in fifteen days, and that's a record for any of us to shoot at."

Later, when Aunt Bess and Uncle Jim and Steve were alone, Uncle Jim said, "I want to confess, Steve, that I've been worried about having you here. I wanted you to be happy, but I knew that a soft white boy from civilization would soon be looked upon by these people with contempt."

contempt—*scorn; a feeling that someone or something is worthless*

He smiled and took Steve firmly by the shoulders. "But I see now I was wrong. I need not have worried. You did what had to be done. You've got the makings of a real Yukon man."

Steve turned away quickly to hide the mist of happiness that had come into his eyes.

Character Theme—Courage & Perseverance

Thinking It Through

1. Why did Sam Ketchum meet Steve in Nenana?

2. Why did Steve decide to go to the Yukon with Sam and the dog team?

3. What did Steve decide to do when the woman at Carlson Creek said that Sam needed a doctor?

4. Why was Steve so happy at the end of the story?

Stopping by Woods on a Snowy Evening

Whose woods these are I think I know.
His house is in the village though;
He will not see me stopping here
To watch his woods fill up with snow.

My little horse must think it queer
To stop without a farmhouse near
Between the woods and frozen lake
The darkest evening of the year.

He gives his harness bells a shake
To ask if there is some mistake.
The only other sound's the sweep
Of easy wind and downy flake.

The woods are lovely, dark and deep,
But I have promises to keep,
And miles to go before I sleep,
And miles to go before I sleep.

—*Robert Frost*

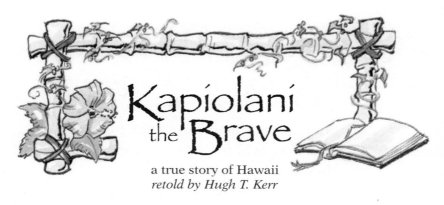

Kapiolani the Brave

a true story of Hawaii
retold by Hugh T. Kerr

"Fear thou not; for I am with thee."—Isaiah 41:10

Long before Hawaii became a state, Kapiolani was a queen of the Hawaiian Islands. She and her people worshiped the false goddess Pele. The Hawaiians thought that Pele lived in the great burning mountain Kilauea.

Whenever the mountain burned and sent up smoke and flame, the priest of Pele came among the people and told them that the goddess was hungry and called for food. Then he would choose someone from among the people to throw into the mouth of the volcano as a peace offering to Pele.

Like the priest of Pele, Kapiolani was ignorant and cruel and superstitious. Then missionaries came to her island with the gospel, and Kapiolani became a real Christian queen. People who had

---

Kapiolani (kăp′ē·ō·lä′nē)
Pele (pē′lē)
Kilauea (kē′lou·ā′ə)—
   an active volcano in Hawaii

superstitious—*believing things out of fear and ignorance rather than basing one's beliefs on the Bible and on scientific findings*

seen her before could not believe she was the same person. She became beautiful and dressed herself neatly and began to help her people.

She took the royal idols which the people worshiped and hid them away in caves so no one could find them. But the people still feared and worshiped Pele, who was supposed to have her home in the burning mountain.

One day, the mountain burned and cast up fire and black smoke, and the old priest came down among the people to choose another sacrifice. Kapiolani met the priest. "There will be no more offerings made to Pele," she declared. The priest was angry, and the mountain burned, and the people were afraid.

Nevertheless, the priest chose his victim, for the people still feared and worshiped the dreadful goddess and were afraid to deny the priest his request. Choosing the choicest youth he could find, the priest led the people up the steep side of the burning mountain.

Kapiolani followed.

She determined that there would be no sacrifice and that she would defy Pele and her priest as Elijah did the priests of Baal on Mount Carmel.

---

defy—*to resist; to oppose openly or boldly*

"Come back, my queen; do not go on!" begged the priest, but she went on.

"Jehovah is my God," Kapiolani said. "I fear not Pele. Should I perish by her anger, then you may fear her powers. But if Jehovah saves me, then you must fear and serve Jehovah." She picked the sacred berries of the mountain, meant only for the goddess, and ate them. As she drew near to the mouth of the smoking mountain, she sang the songs of her Christian faith.

What a brave Christian she was! We must remember that while we know there was nothing to fear from the burning mountain, she had always feared it, and her people still believed in the power of the goddess to harm and destroy. If you will take your Bible and look through it, you will be surprised to find how often God tells His people not to fear. "Fear thou not." "Fear not." "Be not afraid." "Why are ye so fearful?" "Let not your heart be troubled." True religion, which is love, casts out fear. If we only love God enough, we will fear nothing.

The priest trembled, and the people feared, for they thought Pele would strike the queen dead. But Kapiolani was not afraid. She knew that her own God was the only God and that there was no power that could harm her.

God's Spirit spoke to her and said, "Fear thou not: for I am with thee."

Alone she stood upon the edge of the crater. She cast the sacred rod which she had snatched from the old priest's hands into the fire and cried:

"Pele! Here I break your power!
Smite me! Smite me!
Smite me with thy dreadful doom
Smite me, Pele. Smite me."

crater—*the hole at the mouth of a volcano*

smite—*to cause harm*

Nothing happened, and turning to the priest, she said:

"Pele comes not! Is she sleeping?
Is she wandering today?
Is she busy with her burnings,
Is she stricken with decay?"

Then the old priest in his anger cried:

"Smite her, Pele! Pele, smite her!
Smite her with thy dreadful doom!
Smite her, Pele! smite her!"

Still nothing happened, and Kapiolani, turning to the people, who now admired her for her courage, said:

"Hear me, friends.
There is no Pele.
One true God there is!
His this mountain:
His these burnings:
You and I and all things His!
Goodness, mercy, loving-kindness,
Life Eternal, all things His!"

The people were wondering and thinking, and a new hope—the hope of a loving God—was awakening in their hearts. Then the Christian

---

stricken—*afflicted with sickness, pain, or emotion*

queen turned her back upon the burning mountain. Lifting up her hands to heaven, she said:

> "From this day
> Let no man tremble
> When he feels the mountain shake:
> From this day no man or maiden
> Shall be killed for Pele's sake:
> From this day we pass forever
> From the scourge of Pele's rod:
> From this day, Thou, Lord Jehovah,
> Be our one and only God."

In the years that passed, Kapiolani, the Hawaiian queen, helped make her beautiful island a Christian country. She lived a beautiful Christian life and sweetly fell asleep in Jesus.

When we think of her early life and her Christian courage, we, too, feel like saying

> "All hail the power of Jesus' name;
> Let angels prostrate fall.
> Bring forth the royal diadem
> And crown Him Lord of all."

Character Theme—Courage & Faith

---

scourge (skûrj)—*a whipping, or severe punishment*
prostrate—*lying with the face downward to show worship and submission*
diadem—*a crown*

Thinking It Through

1. Why were people thrown into the fiery mouth of the volcano?

2. What did Kapiolani do with the royal idols?

3. Whose life did Kapiolani risk by going up the mountain? Why did she go?

4. What does the phrase she "sweetly fell asleep in Jesus" mean?

5. Kapiolani showed her faith in God by defying the false goddess Pele. What are some things we can do today to show our faith in God?

Two Thousand Miles for a Book

Cynthia Pearl Maus

Many, many years ago, the Nez Perce Indians, who lived in the great Northwest, heard about the white man's Book of Heaven. Traders had told them that some day missionaries would come from the country toward the rising sun with the white man's Bible and tell them all about their wonderful God; and so for years they waited and watched in vain.

Finally it was decided to send five of their braves—three old men and two young ones—on a long journey into the great unknown land beyond the Rocky Mountains in search of the white man's Book of Heaven.

One spring morning, the five braves who had been chosen turned their faces eastward. After two days of hard travel, one of the old men turned back, saying that he was too old to endure the hardships on the way. The others traveled for months, two thousand miles across mountains,

---

Nez Perce (nĕz'pûrs')—*a tribe of Indians living in Idaho, Washington, and Oregon*

in vain—*without success*
endure—*to bear; to put up with*

153

hills, and plains until they reached St. Louis, Missouri, which was then just a small frontier post where a few hundred settlers made their home.

Early one October morning in 1832, these travel-worn Indians saw in the distance the houses of the little settlement. It was the first town they had ever seen; but if they were surprised, they gave no sign. They pushed their silent way through the streets, looking to neither the right nor the left.

General Clark, of the Lewis and Clark expedition many years earlier, was then in command of the fort. When he heard that four strange Indians were without, he sent two officers to bring them in, thinking they had come to make a treaty of some sort. The Indians entered the fort with calm dignity, and after greeting General Clark, took their seats in silence. Days passed, and still these strange messengers said nothing as to the purpose of their journey; but at last they told the meaning of it all: they wanted the white man's Book of Heaven. Would General Clark give it to them? They wanted to know God as the white man knew Him. Would General Clark tell them? They wanted a teacher who would go with them to the land of the Setting Sun, there to break to their people the 'bread of life'—would General Clark send one?

---

dignity—*self-respect*

General Clark hardly knew what to say. He told them all he thought they could understand about the white man's God, but he had no Bible printed in the language those Indians used, and he was not in command of missionaries; and so he could not fully satisfy their strange request.

All winter long the Indians waited and watched, hoping to learn more about the white man's God. During that time General Clark planned amusements for them and did everything he could to make their stay a pleasure. That winter the two old men, weakened by their long journey, sickened and died, and in the spring the two who remained indicated their desire to start again on the long journey back to their people.

General Clark heaped many rich gifts upon them in parting, and on the night before their departure he gave them a great banquet in his own home. When the meal was over, he asked Ta-wis-sis-sim-nim (No Horns on His Head) to address the company. And these are the words which that silent Indian spoke, as translated by an Indian of another tribe who was present at the banquet and who acted as interpreter:

"I came to you over the trail of many moons from the land of the setting sun. . . . My people sent me to get the white man's Book of Heaven.

You took me to where your women dance, as
ours do not, but the Book was not there! You
took me to where they worship the Great Spirit
with candles, but the Book was not there! You
showed me images of the Great Spirit and pictures of the Good Land beyond, but the Book was
not among them to show me the way!

"I am going back over the long trail to my
people who sit in darkness. You make my feet
heavy with gifts and my moccasins will grow old
in carrying them, and yet the Book is not among

them to show me the way! When I tell my people in the big council that I did not bring the Book, no word will be spoken. One by one they will rise up and go out in silence! My people will die in darkness, and they will go on that long journey to other hunting-grounds. No white man will go with them; no white man's Book will make plain the way! I have no more words!"

The homeward journey was made as easy as possible for those two disappointed Indians. They were put on board a Missouri River steamer whose captain took the first "fire-canoe" that ever made that long journey of twenty-two hundred miles to the mouth of the Yellowstone River. Ta-wis-sis-sim-nim, who made that sorrowful speech at the banquet, died near the mouth of the Yellow-stone, so that only one of the four was left to tell the story. He made his way back to his people with a message of cheer on his lips, even if there was a bitter, burning disappointment in his heart. He said: "A white man will be sent with the Book!"

News of the Indians' journey was published in newspapers and magazines, and in 1836, two white men and their wives went to the Northwest with God's Word in answer to the Indians' plea.

---

steamer—*a steamship*

They were Marcus and Narcissa Whitman and Samuel and Eliza Spaulding. In the years that followed, many other missionaries went to show the Indians that the Bible is not the white man's Book, but the Book for all people everywhere and that the Lord of Heaven is not the white man's God, but the God of all who will believe in the saving power of His Son.

Character Theme—Perseverance

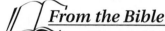

From the Bible

Thy word have I hid in mine heart,
that I might not sin against Thee.
—Psalm 119:11

The law of Thy mouth is better
unto me than thousands of gold
and silver.
—Psalm 119:72

Thy word is a lamp unto my feet, and
a light unto my path.
—Psalm 119:105

Thy word is true from the beginning:
and every one of Thy righteous judg-
ments endureth for ever.
—Psalm 119:160

Thinking It Through

1. How had the Nez Perce Indians heard about the Bible?

2. What town did they come to?

3. What did the Indians want to find?

4. Why do you think the Indians were so disappointed by what they found in St. Louis?

5. Later, who took God's Word to the Indians?

The Heart Test

Sandra Klaus

"Lord Jesus," Mary prayed. "Please help me know what to do tomorrow. I want to please You, but what do I do about Steve?"

Mary set her Bible on the table by her bed and switched the lamp off. But she tossed and turned a long time before going to sleep. The words kept coming back to her: ". . . The Lord seeth not as man seeth; for man looketh on the outward appearance, but the Lord looketh on the heart" (1 Sam. 16:7). "And whatsoever ye do, do it heartily, as to the Lord, and not unto men" (Col. 3:23).

"Hey, Mary," Steve called the next morning as she walked through the front door at school. "I got them! Come here."

Mary walked slowly to where Steve was standing. "Uh, Steve, I've been thinking," she said slowly.

160

Steve acted as if he didn't even hear her. "Here's your copy," he said. "Hide it in your notebook, quick, before anyone sees it." He handed her the sheet and then took off running down the hall.

Not knowing what else to do, Mary stuffed the paper into her notebook. Her heart was racing. What if somebody saw her? How would she explain?

The next day, while she was sitting in class, there was a knock at the classroom door. Mrs. Shuler opened the door and took a note from the office runner. She read it silently and then put it into her pocket.

"Mary and Steve, Mr. Manaheim wants to see you in his office immediately."

Mary looked at Steve in a panic. Steve shrugged and gave her a puzzled look.

"I'll be down in a few minutes," Mrs. Shuler said sternly as they walked past her desk.

On the way to the office, Mary was in tears. "Did you use them?" Mary asked.

Steve looked startled. "Of course I did, didn't you?"

Mary shook her head. "No, I didn't."

"Why not?" Steve stared at her in disbelief. "You said your parents were going to ground you if you didn't get a better grade on your next math test. And my parents told me they were going to take away my video games. I thought we agreed we *had* to pass this math test. That's why I went to so much trouble to get the answers."

Mary looked at the floor. Finally she said, "I know, but I just couldn't."

"What do you mean you couldn't? I gave you the sheet with all the answers on it. Do you mean to tell me you didn't even look at it?"

Mary turned toward the principal's office. "I didn't. But that won't matter now. The page is still in my notebook, and I'm sure Mrs. Shuler is looking for it right now."

Steve's face turned white. "Oh, no," he groaned. "I've still got the answers in my workbook, too."

After they'd been in the principal's office for a few minutes, Mrs. Shuler came in. "Did you find what you were looking for?" Mr. Manaheim asked.

"I did." Mrs. Shuler held up two papers. Both Mary and Steve sank down in their chairs, hoping the floor would swallow them.

"Well?" Mr. Manaheim asked. Folding his arms, he looked right at Mary. "Where did you get this information?"

Steve answered. "She got it from me."

"I'll talk with you later," Mr. Manaheim said
to Steve. Steve had spent a lot of time in the
principal's office. For now, all of Mr. Manaheim's
attention was focused on Mary.

"Mary, why in the world would you cheat like
this? You knew it was wrong, didn't you?"

She looked down, trying to avoid the disappointment in Mr. Manaheim's eyes. "Yes, Sir," she
said. "It's just that my grades in math have been
so bad that I wanted to get good grades again.

My parents told me if I did well on the next test, they'd take me out for pizza. And if I didn't do well, I'd be grounded on school nights. So when Steve came up with the idea, I thought it would make everybody happy. It just seemed like a good idea at the time."

Mrs. Shuler dropped the papers on Mr. Manaheim's desk. "Since when is cheating a good idea?"

Mary bit her lip and was able to stop the tears. "Since never," she choked out. "I knew it was wrong. That's why I didn't look at the answers."

Mr. Manaheim looked at Mrs. Shuler, who shook her head in disbelief.

Mr. Manaheim stared at Mary again. "You're going to sit there and tell me you had the answers but didn't look at them?"

Mary nodded.

Mrs. Shuler was merciless. "Here's the paper. I found it in your notebook!"

Mary was in tears now. "Yes, Ma'am. I did have the paper in my notebook. But I didn't look at it. Honest. Last night, when I was saying my prayers, I remembered a Bible verse I'd learned. It was about how God looks on the inside of people and how people look at the outside. I knew God would be disappointed in me if I cheated, so I didn't. I don't know how to make you believe me, but I didn't cheat."

Mr. Manaheim told her to come back to his office after school was out. He'd tell her then what the punishment would be. He sent her back to class with Mrs. Shuler. Mary could hear Mr. Manaheim questioning Steve as they walked out of the office.

When Steve came back to class, he didn't even look at Mary. Mrs. Shuler gave them the last hour of class as a study time. When the dismissal bell rang, Mary slowly gathered her books and her papers. She also tried to gather her courage before heading back to the principal's office.

Mrs. Shuler stopped her before she got to the door. "Mary," she said. "Are you going to Mr. Manaheim's office?"

"Yes, Ma'am," Mary said sadly.

"Wait, and I'll go with you."

Mary had a strange feeling Mrs. Shuler wasn't as upset as she had been earlier.

When they got to the office, Mr. Manaheim had two desks set up in the corner. "Come right on in." Pointing at the desks, he said to Mary, "This is where you'll be spending your time after school. An hour a day for the next two weeks.

Steve's calling his mother now to tell her. As soon as he gets back, you can call yours."

Mrs. Shuler interrupted. "Mr. Manaheim," she said. "I think we may have been a little hard on Mary today."

Mary's eyes grew wide with surprise.

Mrs. Shuler passed a paper to Mr. Manaheim. It was Mary's math test.

"I've just spent the last hour grading yesterday's math tests," Mrs. Shuler explained. Finally she turned to Mary and smiled. "Mary, I've never been so glad to see such a low test score."

"Perhaps you told us the truth after all," Mr. Manaheim said. "This doesn't look like the test paper of someone who had all the answers."

Mary looked at the graded test. She knew her parents would not be happy with this grade. But she knew, too, that Jesus would be happy with what He saw in her heart!

Mr. Manaheim interrupted her thoughts. "Mary," he asked. "You ride the bus, don't you?"

"Yes," she said.

"Well, then, why don't you hurry? I think you can still catch it. I believe you, but I don't want to see you in my office like this again. Understand?"

"Yes, Sir!" she said, as she grabbed her books. Mrs. Shuler put her hand on her shoulder. "Mary, tomorrow in study hour let's see if we can work together on your math. OK?" Mary nodded her thanks.

Mary raced for the bus and jumped on just as the driver was closing the door. When she landed in her seat, she clutched her books and prayed silently, *Thank You, Lord Jesus, for helping me not to cheat. I love You!*

Character Theme—Honesty

Thinking It Through

1. Who did Mary think would be pleased if she got a good grade on her math test?
2. Where did Mary get the answers to the test?
3. Why did Mary decide not to use the answers?
4. What could Mary have done to have avoided the problem completely?

I'M NOT
ALONE

I'm not alone, though others go
    A different way from what I choose;
I'm not alone, though I say "No!"
    I know that I will never lose.
I'm not alone, though others tease
    And urge that I should go their way;
I'm not alone, though I displease
    My friends by what I'll never say.
I'm not alone, for I now choose—
    Though other folk may call me odd,
Tho' now it seems that I might lose—
    To go the way that Jesus trod.

—*L. E. Dunkin*

The Old Indian Trail

Lillie V. Albrecht

Hannah ran after her brothers. "Wait for me!" she called. "Wait for me!"

"Go back!" cried Parker. "You couldn't go where we're going! No girl could!"

"I could, too!" said Hannah. "I can go anywhere you can go. Where is it?"

"We found an old Indian trail," said Benjamin. "No one knows about it but us."

"Oh, please take me!" cried Hannah. "I promise not to tell anyone about it."

"All right, come if you want to," said Parker. "But I know you will be afraid!"

Hannah followed her brothers as they ran through the woods and began to climb up the mountain. It was a long, hot climb, but at last they all pushed through some brush and came out into the sunlight.

"Come over here," called Benjamin.

Hannah went over to where Benjamin was standing and looked down into a deep, dark gully. "Oh!" she cried, afraid.

"On that other side," said Benjamin, "the trail goes down to the outer fields, where our men are. That's where we're going."

"But—but how do you get over to the other side?" asked Hannah.

"Watch!" said Parker. He stepped back, ran a step, and jumped across the gully.

"Come on!" cried Benjamin. "You can do it, too!" And he jumped after Parker.

Hannah looked down again into the deep, deep, gully. Then she backed away quickly.

"Coward!" cried Parker. "I knew you would be afraid."

"I'm not a coward," said Hannah. "I—I just don't want to jump." She turned and started back down the mountain.

"Coward!" laughed Parker. "Coward!"

The next morning everyone was up early. The men were going to work in the outer fields, and the boys were going fishing. That was a long day for Hannah. She sat with her grandmother in the door yard, waiting for the men and boys to come back.

Then, late in the day, a neighbor came running. "Hurry to the fort!" cried the woman. "Indians are waiting at the river to attack our men as they come from the outer fields!"

"What's to be done?" cried Grandmother. "Is there no way to send word to the men?"

"You must get to the fort as fast as you can!" called the woman. And she ran on to tell the other neighbors.

"What's to be done?" asked Grandmother again after the neighbor had gone. "We can't just go to the fort and leave the men to be attacked."

"If only Parker and Benjamin were here!" cried Hannah. "They could climb over the mountain and tell the men."

"What do you mean?" said Grandmother.

"Well, I wasn't supposed to tell," said Hannah, "but I think I should tell now." Then Hannah told her grandmother about the old Indian trail that went across the gully and down to the outer fields.

"Why can't you go over the mountain yourself, Hannah?" asked Grandmother.

---

door yard—*front yard*

"Oh, no! I can't jump over the gully," said Hannah. "I can't! I'm afraid."

Then Grandmother took Hannah's hands in her own and looked deep into Hannah's eyes. "Listen, Hannah," she said. "I'm an old, old woman. I can't go, but you *must* go. God has called you to save our men, and He will make you strong."

Suddenly Hannah threw her arms around her grandmother. "I'll try!" she said, and in a minute she was on her way.

Hannah hurried up the mountain as fast as she could. When she reached the top of the mountain, she stood for a minute, looking down into the deep gully. She felt she could never, never jump across. Then she thought of her father and all their good neighbors, and of the Indians waiting to attack them. Suddenly Hannah knew that she could not let her father and the other men die like that.

Hannah stepped back and started to run. Then she threw herself forward and sailed across to the other side of the gully. When Hannah picked herself up, her foot hurt and her dress was torn. But she was across! She was across! She hurried down the path to the fields.

Hannah's father could hardly believe his eyes

when he saw her coming. She told him about
the Indians waiting at the river to attack the men.
Then she told him of the old Indian trail over the
mountain.

Her father lost no time in calling the other
workers from the fields. Quickly the men climbed
up the path, and one by one, they jumped across
to the other side.

This time, Hannah made the trip across the
gully in her father's arms.

They reached the fort at nightfall, just as the boys were coming back from fishing.

After supper, all the men and their families sat together quietly in the fort. Then one of the men stood up. "Let us give thanks to God," he said, "for helping one little girl to be strong enough to save so many men."

When the prayer was over, Parker came to the fireplace and stood beside Hannah. "I'll never call you a coward again," he told her softly. . . .

Character Theme—Courage

Thinking It Through

1. Why did Parker and Benjamin not want Hannah to go with them?
2. Why did Grandmother want Hannah to take a message to the men?
3. Why did Hannah jump over the gully that day?
4. Who was probably the most surprised and impressed with what Hannah had done?

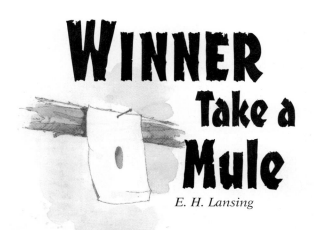

WINNER
Take a
Mule

E. H. Lansing

In the hills where eleven-year-old Jeb
Tillson lived, the dispute he had with mean
Sam Cotter over the ownership of a mule
could easily have led to bloodshed. Jeb's
Uncle Raff challenged Sam to a shooting
match instead, with the winner taking the
mule.

"You men are to shoot at the two targets on
the fence," shouted Mr. Olmstead so everyone
could hear. "Ten shots each, turn and turn about.
Raff take the target to the right. Sam the one to
the left. The man who gets the most shots nearest
his bull's-eye wins."

Every head turned toward the two targets on
the fence. Each one was a square of white paper
with a red circle in its center. Jeb thought the
red circles looked very small. He stood close to
the mule and held tight to the halter rope. He

---

turn and turn about—*one after
another in regular order;
by turns*

halter rope—*a rope tied
around an animal's head
to hold or lead it*

watched Uncle Raff
as he stepped for-
ward to take the first shot. Jeb
heard the report of the gun, but
he couldn't see whether the shot had hit. Then it
was Sam's turn.

Jeb counted the shots. Three for Uncle Raff,
three for Sam. Mr. Olmstead wasn't to look at
the targets until each man had ten shots.

Jeb's hands were stiff from holding the mule's
rope. His eyes ached from trying to see the red
circles. The shots rang in his ears like the crash
of thunder. He lost count of them.

---

report—*a loud, echoing sound*

At last Mr. Olmstead raised his hand. "Ten each," he called. "That's all."

A rustle of talk ran through the crowd as Mr. Olmstead went toward the targets. Jeb closed his eyes and leaned against the mule. But he couldn't keep them closed. He had to know that Uncle Raff had won.

Mr. Olmstead looked from one target to the other. He studied each one so long the crowd grew impatient. Cries of "Who won?" came from every side.

Mr. Olmstead turned to the crowd. "Every one of those shots hit the red circles," he shouted. "The contest's a draw."

A great shout came from the people. Both Uncle Raff and Sam looked very pleased with themselves. But Jeb did not shout. The question of who was to have the mule was still unsettled.

Mr. Olmstead raised his hand for silence. He held up a shining half dollar. "I'll toss this in the air twice. Raff gets first shot at it. Sam second. The one who hits nearest the center wins."

Uncle Raff and Sam nodded agreement. They watched Mr. Olmstead as he stood by the fence with the coin in his hand. Uncle Raff

---

draw—*a tie*

177

limped forward down the slope of the meadow to take his stand for his shot.

Then Jeb caught his breath with a sharp sound. Uncle Raff had slipped and fallen. He landed with a thud on his shooting arm. When he sat up, his arm hung at his side. Jeb dropped the rope and raced to kneel down by Uncle Raff.

"Wrenched bad," said Uncle Raff. His face was tight with pain.

"I win," said Sam in a loud voice. "I win 'cause he can't shoot no more, and I kin."

Uncle Raff did not answer Sam in words. He looked at Jeb and handed him his gun. Jeb knew what he must do. He got to his feet with the gun in his hands.

"I ain't shooting against no boy!" Sam's harsh voice made Jeb jump.

"Don't mind him, Jeb," said Uncle Raff in his easy way. "You got a right to shoot. You're a Tillson."

"I won already!" bellowed Sam.

Mr. Olmstead opened his mouth to speak, but someone got ahead of him. A shrill voice came from the crowd.

---

wrenched—*injured by a sudden twist, pull, or jerk*
bellow—*to cry out loudly in anger or pain*

178

"Don't you pay him no never mind, Jeb Tillson! You kin shoot as good as him any day in the mornin'."

Jeb suddenly felt better. Granny hadn't been able to keep away from the shooting match after all. Now she pushed her way forward through the crowd. Her sharp face was bright with anger.

A loud murmur of approval came from the listening people. Everyone agreed with Granny that Jeb had a right to shoot in Uncle Raff's place.

Mr. Olmstead nodded at Jeb. "Go ahead," he said.

But Sam Cotter was not going to let the crowd have everything its own way. "Iffen I'm to shoot agin a mere boy, I claim the right to shoot first," he said fiercely. "I got some say-so in this shootin' match."

Mr. Olmstead shrugged his shoulders. "I guess Jeb doesn't mind who goes first. Do you, Jeb?"

Jeb shook his head. "I don't mind." He was glad to let Sam shoot first. It would give him time to steady his nerve.

Mr. Olmstead held the coin in his hand, waiting for Sam to give him the signal. Sam lifted his gun to his shoulder, then nodded at

Mr. Olmstead. The coin flew high into the air, a bright flash of silver in the sunshine. Jeb watched the coin, waiting for the sound of Sam's shot. But no sound came.

Sam was holding his gun in both hands, staring angrily at the trigger. "Jammed," muttered Sam, "jammed tighter'n sausage meat."

Uncle Raff chuckled. "Mebbe Jeb wins. He kin shoot and you can't."

Sam glared at Uncle Raff. His own words were coming back to him, and he could think of nothing to say.

Then Jeb moved forward with Uncle Raff's gun in his hands. He did not think what he was doing. But deep in his heart, he wanted to win the mule fairly. He held out Uncle Raff's gun toward Sam.

"Use this gun," said Jeb quietly.

For a long minute, Sam looked at Jeb without moving. Then the hard lines of his jaw softened. "Thanks, boy," said Sam. His voice was as quiet as Jeb's had been. He took the gun and stepped into shooting position.

Once again Sam nodded at Mr. Olmstead. Once again the coin rose in a whirling flash toward the sky. This time, Sam's shot rang out loud and clear. The coin jerked and fell to the ground.

Jeb watched Mr. Olmstead walk toward the place where the coin had fallen. Mr. Olmstead picked up the coin and studied it carefully. Then he held it up to the people. "Nicked off the edge," he cried.

The watching crowd murmured its applause. No one liked Sam well enough to cheer him loudly. But everyone was polite enough to acknowledge a good shot.

Sam did not look at Jeb as he handed back the gun. Jeb clutched the smooth barrel with both hands and walked to the shooting stand. He did not think or feel anything. For a moment his eyes blurred, and he had a horrible fear that he would not even see the coin, much less hit it.

Then he heard a sharp, familiar voice. "Stand up to hit, Jeb. Act like you was glad-proud to be a Tillson."

Granny's brisk words were like a dash of cold water in Jeb's face. His muscles stiffened, and he could think clearly. He turned and grinned at Granny.

Then he lifted the gun and looked at Mr. Olmstead. He saw the tiny coin in Mr. Olmstead's

acknowledge—*to admit to be true; confess*

181

hands. When he gave the signal, it would fly into the air.

Jeb's hands shook. He lowered his gun and looked toward the mule. The mule was watching Jeb. One long ear flapped forward in a friendly greeting.

"Go it, Jeb!" Ben Larkin's high, excited voice sounded very loud to Jeb.

Then another voice spoke. "What you waitin' fer, Jeb?" Uncle Raff's calm, sure words steadied the boy.

He took a firm grip on the rifle. He lifted it to his shoulder and

nodded at Mr.
Olmstead. The
sun caught at the silver
coin. Jeb saw its brightness right
at the end of the gun barrel. His finger
pressed the trigger. Then Jeb shut his eyes.

He didn't open them until he heard a shout
from the people. Then he saw Mr. Olmstead
holding the coin high.

"Right plunk in the middle!" shouted Mr.
Olmstead.

The crowd surged forward and pushed
around Jeb. People thumped him on the back.
Ben jumped up and down like a jack-in-the-box,
yelling with joy. Granny's thin face was stiff with
pride.

---

surge—*to rush forward*

Jeb scarcely felt the thumps on his back. He didn't hear what anyone said. He just stood still and knew the mule was his for keeps.

---

scarcely—*almost did not; barely*

Character Theme—Fairness

Thinking It Through

1. Who got the most shots closer to the bull's-eye, Sam or Uncle Raff?
2. How was the tie to be broken?
3. Why did Sam claim to be the winner?
4. How did Jeb show that he wanted to win fairly?
5. How do you think the mountain people described Jeb after the shooting match?

OUR HEROES

Here's a hand to the boy who has courage
　To do what he knows to be right;
When he falls in the way of temptation,
　He has a hard battle to fight.
Who strives against self and his comrades
　Will find a most powerful foe;
All honor to him if he conquers—
　A cheer for the boy who says "No!"

Be steadfast, my boy, when you're tempted
　And do what you know to be right;
Stand firm by the colors of manhood,
　And you will o'ercome in the fight.
"The Right" be your battle-cry ever,
　In waging the warfare of life;
And God, Who knows who are the heroes,
　Will give you the strength for the strife.

—*Alice and Phoebe Cary*

185

The Middle Bear

Eleanor Estes

Eleanor Estes based her Moffat books on memories of her childhood in the small Connecticut town where she was born. "The Middle Bear" is a chapter from *The Middle Moffat*. You will also enjoy reading *The Moffats* and *Rufus M.*

When a play was given at the Town Hall, Sylvie was usually the only one of the four Moffats who was in it. However, once in a while the others were in a play. For instance, Rufus had been the smallest of the seven dwarfs. And once Janey had been a butterfly. She had not been an altogether successful butterfly, though, for she had tripped on the sole of her stocking, turning a somersault all across the stage. And whereas Joey was rarely in a play, he was often in charge of switching the lights on and off.

Now there was to be a play at the Town Hall, "The Three Bears," and all four of the Moffats were going to be in it. Miss Chichester, the school

Chichester (chē′chĕs·tẽr)

teacher, was putting it on. But the money for the tickets was not going into her pocket or into the Moffats' pocket, even though they were all in the play. The money was to help pay for the new parish house. The old one had burned down last May and now a new one was being built. "The Three Bears" was to help raise the money to finish it. A benefit performance, it was called.

In this benefit performance, Sylvie was to play the part of Goldilocks. Joey was to be the big bear, Rufus the little bear, and Janey the middle bear. Jane had not asked to be the middle bear. It just naturally came out that way. The middle Moffat was going to be the middle bear.

As a rule, Joey did not enjoy the idea of acting in a play; however, he felt this play would be different. He felt it would be like having a disguise on, to be inside of a bear costume. And Jane felt the same way. She thought the people in the audience would not recognize her as the butterfly who turned a somersault across the stage, because she would be comfortably hidden inside her brown bear costume. As for Rufus, he hoped that Sylvie, the Goldilocks of this game, would not sit down too hard on that nice little chair of his and really

---

parish house—*a church building used for socials, children's meetings, etc.*

break it to bits. It was such a good chair, and he wished he had it at home.

Mama was making all the costumes, even the bear heads. A big one for Joey, a little one for Rufus, and a middle-sized one for Jane. Of course, she wasn't making them out of bear fur; she was using brown flannel.

Now Jane was trying on her middle-bear costume. She stepped into the body of the costume, and then Mama put the head on her.

"Make the holes for the eyes big enough," Jane begged. "So I'll see where I'm going and won't turn somersaults."

"Well," said Mama, "if I cut the eyes any larger, you will look like a deep-sea diver instead of a bear."

"Oh, well . . ." said Jane hastily. "A bear's got to look like a bear. Never mind making them bigger, then."

Besides being in the play, each of the Moffats also had ten tickets to sell. And since Rufus really was too little to go from house to house and street to street selling tickets, the other three Moffats had even more to dispose of. Forty tickets!

At first Jane wondered if a girl should sell tickets to a play she was going to be in. Was that being conceited? Well, since the money was for the new parish house and not for the Moffats, she finally decided it was all right to sell the tickets. Besides, she thought, who would recognize her as the girl who sold tickets once she was inside her bear costume?

Sylvie sold most of her tickets like lightning to the ladies in the choir. But Joey's and Janey's tickets became grimier and grimier, they had such trouble disposing of them. Nancy Stokes said she would help, even though she went to a different parish house. She and Joey and Jane went quietly and politely up on people's verandas and rang the bell.

"Buy a ticket for the benefit of the new parish house?" was all they meant to say. But very often no one at all answered the bell.

"They can't all be away," said Nancy. "Do you think they hide behind the curtains when they see us coming?"

---

conceited—*prideful; vain*
grimy—*smudged all over with dirt*

"Oh no," said Jane. "You see it'd be different if the money was for us. But it isn't. It's a benefit. Why should they hide?"

One lady said she was very sorry but she was making mincemeat. "See?" she said, holding up her hand. They were all covered with mincemeat. So she could not buy a ticket. Not possibly, and she closed the door in their faces.

"She could wash her hands," said Nancy angrily. The children called this lady "mincement," ever after. Of course, she never knew it.

Yes, the tickets were very hard to sell. But little by little the pile did dwindle. If only everybody were like Mrs. Stokes, they would go very fast. She bought four tickets! Jane was embarrassed.

"Tell your mother she doesn't have to buy all those tickets just 'cause all of us are in the play," she instructed Nancy.

But all the Stokeses insisted they really wanted to go. And even if none of the Moffats were in it, they would still want to go, for the play would help to build a new parish house. What nice people! thought Jane. Here they were, a family who went to the brick church, buying tickets to help build a parish house for Janey's church. She

---

mincemeat—*a mixture of chopped apples, spices, raisins, etc., used as pie filling*   dwindle—*to become smaller*

hoped she would be a good middle bear, so they would be proud they knew her.

At last, it was the night of the play. The four Moffats knew their lines perfectly. This was not surprising, considering they all lived in the same house and could practice their lines any time they wanted to. And, besides this, they had had two rehearsals, one in regular clothes and one in their bear costumes.

When Jane reached the Town Hall, she was surprised to find there were many features on the program besides "The Three Bears." The Gillespie twins were going to give a piano duet. "By the Brook," it was called. A boy was going to play the violin. And Miss Beale was going to sing a song. A big program. And the Moffats, all of them except Mama, were going to watch this whole performance from behind the scenes. They could not sit in the audience with the regular people with their bear costumes on, for that would give the whole show away.

Jane fastened her eye to a hole in the curtain. Mama had not yet come. Of course Mama would have to sit out front there with the regular people, even though she had made the costumes. The only people who had arrived so far were Clara Pringle and Brud. They were sitting in the front row, and Jane wondered how they had gotten in, because the front door that all the regular people were supposed to use wasn't even open yet.

When Jane wasn't peering through a hole in the curtain, Joey or Rufus was. Each one hoped he would be the first to see Mama when she came in. Or now and then, they tried to squeeze through the opening at the side of the curtain. But the gnarled little janitor shook his head at them. So they stayed inside.

Sylvie was busy putting make-up on. Jane watched enviously. The only trouble with wearing a bear costume, she thought, was that she couldn't have her face painted. Well, she quickly consoled herself, she certainly would not have stage fright inside her bear head. Whereas she might if there were just paint on her face. "Somebody has been sitting in my chair," she rehearsed her lines. She stepped into her bear costume. But before putting on her head, she helped Rufus into *his* bear uniform. He didn't call it a costume. A uniform. A bear uniform. Jane set his head on his shoulders, found his two eyes for him so he could see out, and the little bear was ready.

---

gnarled—*twisted; bent over, as with age*   consoled—*comforted*

Joey had no difficulty stepping into his costume and in finding his own two eyes. Now the big bear and the little bear were ready. Jane looked around for her head, to put it on. Where was it?

"Where's my head?" she asked. "My bear head."

Nobody paid any attention to her. Miss Chichester was running back and forth and all around, giving an order here and an order there. Once, as she rushed by, causing a great breeze, Jane yelled to make herself heard, "How can we act 'The Three Bears' unless I find my middle-bear head?"

"Not just now; I'm too busy," was all Miss Chichester said.

Everybody was too busy to help Jane find her head. Sylvie was busy helping someone else dress. Joey was busy running around doing this and doing that for Miss Chichester. And the little old janitor was busy tightening ropes and making sure the lights were working. Rufus could not be torn from a hole in the curtain. He was looking for Mama.

Jane sighed. Everybody is busy, she thought. She rummaged around in a big box of costumes. Maybe her bear head had been stuck into it. She found a dragon head and tried it on. How would that be? She looked in the mirror. The effect was interesting. But, no, she could not wear this, for a bear cannot be a dragon.

A Headless Bear

Goodness, thought Jane. The curtain will go up, and the middle bear won't be a whole bear. This was worse than tripping over her stocking the time she was a butterfly. Maybe Joey and Rufus somehow or another had two heads on. They didn't, though, just their own. Phew, it was warm inside these bear costumes. Jane stood beside Rufus and looked through another small hole in the curtain. Oh! The big door was open! People were beginning to arrive. And what kind of a bear would she be without a head? Maybe she wouldn't be allowed to be a bear at all. But there certainly could not be three bears without a middle one.

"Don't worry," said Rufus, not moving an inch from his spot. "Lend you mine for half the play . . ."

"Thanks," said Jane. "But we all have to have our heads on all through the whole thing."

The Stokeses were coming in! Jane felt worried. The only person who might be able to fix a new bear head for her in a hurry was Mama. Oh, if she had only made a couple of spare heads! But

Mama wasn't coming yet. Jane resolved to go and meet her. She put on her hat and her winter coat over her bear costume. Then she ran down the three narrow steps into the Hall. She crouched low in her coat in order not to give away the fact that she was clad in a bear costume. Nobody on this side of the curtain was supposed to know what people on her side of the curtain had on until the curtain rolled up. Surprise. That's what was important in a play.

Mr. Buckle was coming in now, walking towards the front row. Jane stooped low, with her knees bent beneath her. In front her coat nearly reached the ground. From the way she looked from the front, few would guess that she was the

resolved—*made a firm decision*   clad—*dressed*

middle bear. Of course, her feet showed. They were encased in the brown costume. But she might be a brownie or even a squirrel.

"Hello, Mr. Buckle," said Jane. "I'm in a hurry. . . ."

"Where are you going, middle Moffat?" he asked. "Aren't you the prima donna?"

"No, just the middle bear."

"Well, that's fine. The middle Moffat is the middle bear."

"Yes. Or I was until I lost my head."

"Oh, my," said Mr. Buckle. "This, then is not your head?" he asked, pointing to her hat.

"Yes, but not my bear head. I don't mean bare head. Bear head! B-e-a-r. That kind of head."

"Mystifying. Very mystifying," said Mr. Buckle, settling himself slowly in a seat in the front row.

"You'll see later," said Jane, running down the aisle.

She ran all the way home. But the house was dark. Mama had already left. And she must have gone around the other way, or Jane would have passed her. Jane raced back to the Town

---

prima donna (prē′mə dŏn′ə)—*the most important woman singer in an opera or concert*

Hall. There! Now! The lights were dim. The entertainment had begun. Jane tried to open the side door. Chief Mulligan was guarding this entrance. He did not want to let her in at first. He thought she was just a person. But when she showed him her costume, he opened the door just wide enough for her. The bear costume was as good as a password.

Jane tiptoed up the three steps and went backstage, wondering what would happen now. The show always goes on. There was some comfort in that thought. Somehow, someone would fix her head. Or possibly, while she was gone, her middle bear head had been found. She hoped she would not have to act with her head bare.

Miss Chichester snatched her.

"Oh, there you are, Jane! Hop into your costume, dear."

"I'm in it," said Jane. "But I can't find my middle-bear head."

"What else can go wrong?" said Miss Chichester, grasping her own head.

Jane looked at her in surprise. What else *had* gone wrong? Had others lost worse than their heads?

"Where's the janitor?" Miss Chichester asked. "Maybe he let his grandchildren borrow it."

Jane knew he hadn't, but she couldn't tell Miss Chichester, for she had already flown off. And then Janey had an idea.

"I know what," she said to Joey. "Pin me together." And she pulled the neck part of her costume up over her head. Joey pinned it with two safety pins, and he cut two holes for her eyes. This costume was not comfortable now. Pulling it up and pinning it this way lifted Jane's arms so she had trouble making them hang down the way she thought a bear's should. However, at any rate, she now had a bear head of sorts.

"Do I look like a bear?" she asked Rufus.

"You look like a brown ghost," Rufus replied.

"Don't you worry," said Sylvie, coming up. "You look like a very nice little animal."

"But I'm supposed to be a bear, not a nice little animal," said Jane.

"Well," said Sylvie, "people will know you are supposed to be a bear, because Rufus and Joey both have their bear heads on."

So Jane resigned herself to not being a perfect bear. She tried to comfort herself with the thought that she would still be in disguise. She hoped her acting would be so good it would

---

resign—*to submit to or accept circumstances*

counterbalance her bad head. "Somebody has been eating my porridge," she practiced.

Miss Chichester appeared. "The janitor said 'No,'" she said. She thoughtfully surveyed Jane a moment. "Hm-m-m, a makeshift," she observed. "Well, it's better than nothing," she agreed with Jane. But she decided to switch the order of the program around in order to give everybody one last chance to find the middle-bear's head. She sent Miss Beale out onto the stage. Everybody hoped that while Miss Beale was singing, "In an Old-fashioned Garden," the head would appear. But it didn't.

"Keep a little in the background," said Miss Chichester to Jane. "Perhaps people will not notice."

"If I can only see where the background is," thought Jane. For she found it even harder to keep her eyes close to the holes cut in her costume than it had been to the real ones in her regular bear head.

Now the heavy curtain rolled up. It didn't stick halfway up as it sometimes did, and Sylvie, Goldilocks, in a blue pinafore and socks, ran out onto the stage amidst loud applause. The play

---

counterbalance—*to offset; make up for*
makeshift—*a last-minute arrangement*

had begun! Sylvie had a great deal of acting to do all by herself before the three bears came home. But she wasn't scared. She was used to being on the stage alone.

The Show Must Go On

Jane's heart pounded as she and Joey and Rufus waited for their cue to come home. If only she didn't trip and turn a somersault!—for she really could not see very well. Somehow she managed to see out of only one eye at a time. These eyeholes must have been cut crooked. One hole kept getting hooked on her nose.

"Now!" Miss Chichester whispered. "Cue! Out with you three bears."

Joe, Jane, and Rufus, the three bears, lumbered out onto the stage. They were never supposed to just walk, always lumber and lope.

The applause was tremendous. It startled the three bears. The Town Hall was packed. Somebody must have sold a lot of tickets.

"There's Mama," said Rufus. He said it out loud.

He wasn't supposed to say anything out loud except about his porridge, his chair, and his bed. But anyway he said, "There's Mama." Jane could

lumber—*to move heavily and clumsily*
lope—*to move along with a swinging stride*

not see Mama. Lumbering out onto the stage had dislocated her costume, so that now she could not see at all. Fortunately, the footlights shone through the brown flannel of her costume so she could keep away from the edge of the stage and not fall off.

The Moffats all knew their lines so well they did not forget them once. The only trouble was they did not have much chance to say them, because the applause was so great every time they opened their mouths. At last, however, they reached the act about the three beds. An extra platform had been set up on the stage to look like the upstairs of a three bears' house. The three bears lumbered slowly up the steps.

Suddenly, shouts arose all over the Hall:

"Her head! Her head! The middle-bear's head!"

"Sh-sh-sh," said others. "See what's going to happen."

As Jane could not see very well, she had no idea what these shouts referred to. She had the same head on now that she had had on all during this play so far. Why then all these shouts? Or had she really stayed in the background the way Miss Chichester had asked her to, and the audience had only just discovered the makeshift?

"Oh," whispered Joey to Jane. "I see it. It's your real bear head, and it's on the top of my bedpost."

"O-o-o-h!" said Jane. "Get it down."

"How can I?" said Joe. "With all these people watching me?"

"Try and get it when you punch your bed," urged Jane.

Joey was examining his big bear's bed now. "Hm-m-m," he said fiercely. "Somebody had been lying on my bed. . . ." But he couldn't reach the middle-bear's head. He did try. But he couldn't quite reach it, and there was more laughter from the audience.

Jane pulled her costume about until she could see through the eyehole. Ah, there was her head! On the post of the big bear's bed. No wonder people were laughing. What a place for the middle-bear's head! Here she was, without it. And there it was, without her. Jane resolved to get it. Somehow or other she would rescue her head before this play was completely over. Now was her chance. It was her turn to talk about her bed. Instead, Jane said:

"Somebody has been trying on my head, and there it is!"

Jane hopped up on Joey's bed. She grabbed her middle-bear head.

"Yes," she repeated. "Somebody has been

trying on my head," but as she added, "and here
it is!" the safety pins that held her makeshift
head together popped open. The audience burst
into roars of laughter as Janey's own real head
emerged. Only for a second, though. For she

clapped her middle-bear head right on as fast as she could, and hopped off the bed. Goodness, she thought, I showed my real face, and I didn't have any paint on it.

Unfortunately, Jane still could not see, for she had stuck her bear head on backwards. But the audience loved it. They clapped and they stamped. Bravo! Bravo! Bravo, middle bear! Big boys at the back of the hall put their fingers in their mouths and whistled. And it was a long time before Jane could say:

"Somebody has been sleeping in my bed," and the play could go on. At last, Rufus discovered Goldilocks in his little bed, and she leaped out of the window. That was the end of the play, and the curtain rolled down.

When the bowing began, Miss Chichester tried to send Jane in backwards, thinking the back of her was the front of her. Fortunately, Rufus held Jane by one paw, and Joey held the other. So she didn't get lost. And the three bears lumbered dizzily on and off many times, sometimes with Sylvie, and sometimes alone. And somebody yelled for "The mysterious middle bear!" It must have been the oldest inhabitant.

Miss Chichester turned Jane's head around

emerge—*to come into view*

204

for this bow, and at last Jane really did look like a
perfect middle bear. Furthermore, she could see
out. There was Mama, laughing so hard the tears
were rolling down her cheeks. And there was
Nancy Stokes with all the Stokeses, and Olga was
there. And there was Mr. Buckle, beaming up
at the stage. Jane bowed and lumbered off the
stage. She felt good now. Acting was fun, she
thought, especially if you could be disguised in a
bear uniform. And this time she had not turned
a somersault across the stage as she had the time
she was a butterfly. True, she had lost her head.
But she had found it. And the show had gone on,
the way people always say shows do.

Moreover, the Moffats had nice warm bear pajamas to sleep in for the rest of the winter. Of course, they didn't go to bed with the bear heads on. But the rest of the costumes were nice and warm.

Character Theme—Resourcefulness

Thinking It Through

1. Why was the play, *The Three Bears,* being given?

2. Why did Joey and Jane not feel self-conscious about being in this play?

3. After searching frantically for her bear head when it was time for the play, where did Jane finally see it?

4. How did Jane make sure that the play went on?

FURRY BEAR

If I were a bear,
  And a big bear too,
I shouldn't much care
  If it froze or snew;
I shouldn't much mind
  If it snowed or friz—
I'd be all fur-lined
  With a coat like his!

For I'd have fur boots and a brown fur wrap,
And brown fur knickers and a big fur cap.
I'd have a fur muffle-ruff to cover my jaws,
And brown fur mittens on my big brown paws.
With a big brown furry-down up to my head,
I'd sleep all the winter in a big fur bed.

—*A. A. Milne*

knickers—*short pants*
  that gather at the knee

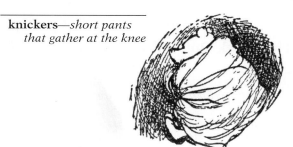

CITRONELLA WEATHER

Mildred Lawrence

Growing up in a newspaper-publishing family in the 1940s was exciting for Malinda Rebel. She did wish, however, that there was something she could do to help with the paper.

"Hush, Malinda!" said Mother. "Daddy's writing an editorial."

Malinda hushed. When Daddy was writing an editorial, he absolutely, positively, must not be disturbed. But she did wish, when everybody else in the Rebel family had their name on the masthead of the *Argus*, that she could have hers there, too.

"Randolph Rebel, Editor and Publisher," it began. (That, of course, was Daddy.)

"Mrs. Randolph Rebel, Society Editor." (And that, of course, was Mother.)

"Junius Rebel, Advertising Manager." (Junius, Malinda's oldest brother, wrote things that said, "On Sale! This Week Only! Boots and Galoshes!")

---

editorial—*a statement of opinion in a newspaper, usually written by an editor*
masthead—*information box listing the owners, editors, price, etc.*

galoshes—*waterproof overshoes*

"Jeremy Rebel, Custodian." (Jeremy, Malinda's second oldest brother, swept out the office and helped run the printing press when Big Eph didn't get there.)

"David Rebel, Circulation Manager." (David, Malinda's third-oldest brother, delivered all the papers every week.)

Only Malinda wasn't anybody at all. It made her feel very lonesome, like the orphan children that Mother sent the barrel of old clothes to every year.

"Please, please Daddy," begged Malinda, "can't I do something too?"

"You're not old enough, Baby," said Daddy vaguely. But Malinda kept practicing writing news items and taking them out into the back room where Mr. Wooliver was setting type. Malinda liked talking to Mr. Wooliver. He was never too busy to pay attention. Besides, by sniffing around where Mr. Wooliver was, she could tell what the weather was that day.

If it was cold, Mr. Wooliver had a roll of cotton soaked in camphor behind each ear—"to ward off colds," he said. If it was warm, the cotton was soaked in citronella to keep the mosquitoes away.

---

custodian—*a janitor*
camphor—*a strong-smelling crystal or oil, used to protect clothes from moths*

citronella—*a strong-smelling oil used in insect repellants*

"I never catch colds and I never get mosquito bites," said Mr. Wooliver, wiping enough ink off his hands so that he could pick up Malinda's news items.

"'Annabelle Douglas's cat, Mee-Yow, has six baby kittens,'" he read. " 'One of them has six toes on its front feet.' Well, now, that's very good, young miss. Going to be a writer like your dad, I see."

And so Malinda ran happily back to her favorite bench in the park and wrote down some more news.

"Clarinda Smith and Robby Holcomb found a hornets' nest down by the river last week," she wrote. "The hornets were not glad to see them. They got stung eight times."

She nibbled her pencil and looked down at the river far below. Nearly everybody in Riverdale lived down on the river bank. But the stores, and the churches, and the city hall, and the library were all at the top of the hill, a long climb even for Malinda.

"Lucius Wixby fell into the river Tuesday," wrote Malinda, "and spoiled his new suit that his mother bought at the bargain sale last week."

She ran back to the *Argus* to see if just this once her father would print some of her news items. But she had forgotten that this was the day when the rest of the family were going to the Press Club meeting at Highlands, across the river and sixty miles away. Malinda was to stay home with Great-aunt Essie.

Daddy rattled out a last-minute news item, Mother finished reading the last galley proof, and Junius made a correction on the general store's advertisement so that it would say that coats, not goats, were on sale at $14.95. Mr. Rebel took his news item out to Mr. Wooliver, who was wearing camphor that day, even though it was very springlike outside.

"Leave a place on the front page for the Press Club report," said Daddy. "I'll write it when I get home. You're the boss while I'm gone."

Mr. Wooliver winked at Malinda. "In that case, I'll ask the young miss to help me today," he said. "I'll have my hands full, seeing tomorrow's press day."

"Anything you like," said Daddy. "Good-bye, Baby."

Malinda did wish her father wouldn't call her Baby, but Mr. Wooliver seemed not to hear.

"Now, young miss," he said, settling the little rolls of camphor-cotton more securely behind his

---

galley proof—*a trial printing of a page
so it can be checked for spelling, etc.*

211

ears, "I have a feeling in my bones that it's going to rain. I favor your hurrying home for your boots and raincoat."

"Yes, sir," said Malinda.

"Oh, yes, and tell your Great-aunt Essie that you won't be home until after supper. The day before press day is a pretty busy day, but I think we can manage—that is, with the two of us."

"It's pouring down rain," said Malinda when she came back, puffing from the climb up the hill. "You were right. Camphor was just right for today."

"I very seldom miss," said Mr. Wooliver. "Let me see, now! Would you like to take these handbills over to the auctioneer? He's in a hurry for them."

Malinda scampered off. It was raining harder than ever now. The low place on the corner where the

___

handbill—*a small printed notice or advertisement; passed out by hand*

rain collected during every storm already looked like a small lake.

"Now you may put some of these leads between each line on this front-page story," said Mr. Wooliver, when she returned. "The leads, you know, are what make the fresh air between the rows of type."

Why, even the boys weren't allowed to touch Mr. Wooliver's type!

"You're so nice," said Malinda. "I'm having the best time!"

"I have to have help," said Mr. Wooliver gruffly. "Can't get this paper out all by myself. Now, then, will you answer the telephone?"

It was somebody from out in the country wanting to know if Malinda knew anything about a flood.

"No," said Malinda politely, "we don't. But it's raining quite hard."

It must have been raining harder than Malinda imagined, because pretty soon Great-aunt Essie called up to tell Malinda to stay on the hill.

"Been trying to get you for an hour," said Great-aunt Essie, who sounded like a sputtering firecracker when she was excited. "Radio says everybody get out of the valley on account of the flood. Water's already halfway up the basement steps. It put the furnace fire out. I'll be at the church. The Ladies' Aid's going to serve supper for everybody."

"Wh-what about Mother and D-daddy?" asked Malinda, but Great-aunt Essie had already hung up.

"They'll be all right," said Mr. Wooliver, who had been listening over her shoulder. "They're at Highlands, safe and sound. It's a good thing you're here and not there, busy as I am! Now, then, people will be calling up here to see where to go and where to sleep and all. Better call up the mayor and see what to tell them."

Malinda put in a very busy afternoon. The telephone rang every five mintues, and people came in to ask questions. And all the time it kept on raining.

"Radio says the road from Highlands is closed," Mr. Wooliver reported. "Looks as though we'll have to get this paper out by ourselves." Both Malinda and Mr. Wooliver knew very well that the *Argus* couldn't miss its publication day, flood or no flood.

"Good thing they wrote everything before they left, for writing is not my line," said Mr. Wooliver, counting pages. "One, two, three, four, five, six, seven—oh, no! There's that big gap in the front page."

Malinda looked at the streamer at the top of Page One. *"Riverdale Argus,"* it said. "We Get the News."

"I think we should telephone Daddy," Malinda decided. "It says we get the news, and the flood is news, and Daddy won't like it if it's not in the paper."

"Long-distance telephone lines are out," said Mr. Wooliver gloomily.

There was a long pause while Malinda thought very hard. "Daddy won't let me write for the paper," she said, "on account of being too young."

There was another long pause. "But I guess I'll have to," she decided, "since I'm the only one in the family that's home."

"Quite right, too, young miss," said Mr. Wooliver. "And you'd better start now."

Malinda nibbled her pencil and tried to remember all the things that she had heard about the flood and also all the things that Daddy had told the boys about how to write stories for the *Argus*.

"Put the most important things first," Daddy always said, "in case you might not have room for the rest."

---

streamer—*a newspaper headline that goes across a full page*

"Everybody in Riverdale is up on the Hill," wrote Malinda, "on account of the big flood. People are eating at the church and sleeping in the city hall and the library. . . .

"Mrs. Eustace said her clothes basket was floating around in her basement like a boat.

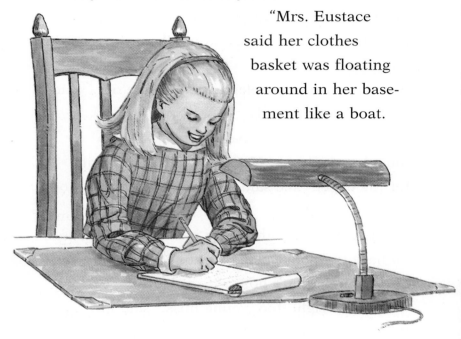

Annabelle Douglas's cat, Mee-Yow, led her six kittens up the Hill to the firehouse. Spotty, the fire department dog, does not like so many cats there.

"The Mayor says he thinks that people can go home in another day. Mrs. Ransome said she hoped so, because she wanted to take down her wash, which was hanging in the basement. It is under water now, but Mrs. Ransome says for once her wash got plenty of rinsing in fresh rain water."

Before Malinda knew it, it was time to go to the church for supper.

"You sleep on the couch in Daddy's office," Malinda told Great-aunt Essie. "I can sleep on his desk."

"I know a better place than that," said Mr. Wooliver. "Sleep on the press. More room to turn over."

As she fell asleep, Malinda could hear Mr. Wooliver setting the type for her story about the flood. And then she didn't remember a thing until Mr. Wooliver was shaking her to wake her up.

"Big Eph's here, young miss," he said, "and we can't print the paper with little girls asleep on the press. Rain's settled down to a drizzle, and the water's starting to go down. You go to the church and get your breakfast, and then scoot along to school."

When Malinda came back from school in the afternoon, Daddy and Mother and Junius and Jeremy and David were all there. There was a neat stack of new papers on the counter. Malinda gave everybody a big hug.

---

setting type—*arranging type for printing; today usually done by computer*

"Did you have a good time?" she asked. "I slept on the press. And I helped Mr. Wooliver. And I—"

Suddenly she caught sight of the paper and the big headline which said, "Flood Routs Riverdale Residents." Right at the beginning of her story were the words, "By Malinda Rebel."

Malinda gasped. Why, even the boys had never had a by-line! She did hope that Daddy wouldn't be cross with Mr. Wooliver. "Daddy," she said, "did we do right? We couldn't get you and—"

---

routs—*forces to leave*
by-line—*a line at the top of a magazine or newspaper article telling who wrote it*

"Hush, Malinda," said Mother. "Daddy's writing an editorial."

"You come and sit beside me while I write it," said Daddy. "It's about you."

Malinda leaned her chin against Daddy's shoulder. Beside his typewriter lay a proof of the masthead. A new name had been added: "Malinda Rebel, Reporter."

"Oh, Daddy!" said Malinda.

But Mr. Rebel's typewriter was going clickety-clack.

"A Chip Off the Old Block," wrote Daddy. Then, "I'm a proud man today, and for once I am going to brag about one of my children. My daughter, Malinda—"

"Oh, Daddy!" said Malinda again.

Why, even the boys had never had an editorial written about them! Mother and Junius and Jeremy and David all stood around and watched Daddy while he wrote. Even Mr. Wooliver came in and peered over his glasses. In spite of the drizzle outside, Malinda knew that it was going to be a lovely day, because Mr. Wooliver smelled like an extra-large bottle of citronella.

Character Theme—Industry & Initiative

219

Thinking It Through

1. How often did the Rebel family publish their newspaper?

2. Why was Malinda the only one whose name was not on the masthead?

3. Where were Malinda's parents and brothers when the flood came?

4. Why did Malinda decide she had to write the article about the flood?

5. How did Mr. Wooliver and Mr. Rebel show that they were proud of Malinda?

The President's Whiskers

Hertha Pauli

In 1860, a girl named Grace Bedell wrote to Abraham Lincoln saying she thought he would look better and get more votes if he had whiskers. Lincoln, who was running for President at the time, sent Grace a friendly reply but did not say whether he would act upon her advice. Mr. Lincoln won the election, and Grace was filled with excitement because the train carrying him to Washington, D.C., was scheduled to stop near her home in New York State. Now she would be able to see the great man himself. Would he have whiskers?

The unforgettable date was February 16, 1861. On February 16, a special train would stop a few miles from Westfield—the train that was carrying Mr. Lincoln to the White House.

Grace hardly slept the night before. It was pitch dark when she wriggled into the sky-blue percale with the polka dots—her Sunday dress. She held the oil lamp up to the small mirror. Did she look like a real lady? No, the bonnet was missing. It had velvet ribbons and two pink

---

Bedell (bĕd′əl)   **percale**—*fine, closely woven cotton cloth*

flowers on top. In a moment, a perfect little lady smiled out of the mirror, and the flowers nodded approval.

The lady was satisfied. She put the lamp back on the table and leaned on the window sill, waiting impatiently for dawn to break.

Other windows began to light up in the village. Grace heard voices in the house, and the clatter of pots and pans. She got her warm cape and took a last look out the window. A few high clouds were sailing slowly southward. It would be a beautiful day.

Downstairs, Mother was washing the dishes. Grace danced through the room. "Mother, does my skirt hang right?"

"Stand still a moment. Now turn, slowly. Yes, it's straight all around."

Grace's face fell suddenly. "There'll be so many people he won't even see me," she pouted.

"You're lucky to see him, dear," Mother said.

It was not yet sunup when the Bedells set out in the spring wagon. The older boys had gone ahead, but the rest of them sat under the tasseled top: Father holding the reins, Mother, Grace, Sam, even Kitty. The baby came along, too, asleep in Mother's arms, because Father insisted. "When she grows up," he said, "she'll want to tell she saw him, and she may not get another chance."

Grace could not sit still. "Look—" she pointed, jumping up and down triumphantly—"there are the Rices, but Bricktop is going to school today—"

If Grace was not quiet, Father said over his shoulder, *she* would be going to school today.

"Will you hold the baby awhile, dear?" Mother asked. Grace held the baby. She held it so quietly it did not even wake up.

Horses and vehicles crowded Main and North Portage streets. For days, Westfield had been in a dither; today it would be deserted. Shops were shut. On the post office door hung a big sign: "Closed for Business on February 16."

"Look at the crowd!" said Mother. "Do drive carefully, Father."

The horse-and-buggy parade moved out of the village and westward. Harnesses glistened in the

---

dither—*a nervously excited or confused condition*

rising sun. Now and then, a farmer's wagon fell in from a side road, or a couple of men on horseback. There were more people on the road than for the fair.

They entered North East, crossing the tracks in the center of the village. Another turn, and there was the depot, decked in red-white-and-blue bunting, with "Hail to the Chief" spelled out in big letters on a streamer across the tracks.

Mr. Bedell tied the horses to the hitchrail and put blankets on them so they would not freeze. The family headed for the depot, only to find a line of soldiers around it and no one permitted to pass except people with ribbons in their buttonholes. The Bedells had to stand in the crowd. Mother said they were lucky the ground was frozen or their dresses would be ruined.

Then—"They're coming!" Grace screamed.

Wagons came clattering up the road. Men jumped off and lined up as for a drill on the green. The fifes and drums played. There were the three older Bedell boys, and in front of them, barking commands just as if he were in the classroom, was Mr. Wedge! Grace felt actually proud of the assistant principal. Then came the carriages, led by

---

bunting—*a thin cloth used in making flags, streamers, etc.*

depot—*a railroad or bus station*

Mr. Rice's. Mr. Rice drove his chestnuts himself, with a tall, gleaming stovepipe hat of black silk on his head. All the carriages were full of silk hats and beribboned buttonholes. Father explained that these marks distinguished the reception committee for Mr. Lincoln.

The crowd was still growing. People kept pushing in front until Grace hardly saw the depot any more. Even the flag on the roof disappeared from time to time behind the feathered hat of a large lady.

Baby Sue started to cry, and Mother went back to the wagon with her and Kitty and Sam. Only Father stayed with Grace. They were far back in the crowd now.

"Will he come now?" she asked.

Mr. Bedell drew out his watch. "If the paper had the schedule right, the train is due in an hour."

It was the longest hour in Grace's life.

A gull shrieked. Or—? There was a sudden hush. The shriek came again. It was no gull. It was a steam whistle.

"Here she comes!" And everybody started pushing and craning necks. Grace held onto Father's hand. And yet she was swept forward and sideways and back. People began to yell, to cheer. Grace

distinguish—*to set apart*

saw small clouds of black smoke rise into the blue sky, closer and closer. She stretched as high on her toes as she could and saw the top of a huge black funnel pass slowly behind many heads, hissing and puffing smoke, and then the flat roof of a car, and another, and a third with the Stars and Stripes fluttering over the rear platform.

The hat in front shifted a little. Grace had a glimpse of the platform. The noise was deafening.

When a Dream Comes True

One of the stovepipe hats had risen above the rest. A very tall, very black hat, quietly sticking out of a lot of fidgety black hats—this was all Grace could see, until the lady in front got so excited that her feathered headgear slipped to one side. Then she saw more. The calm hat was not half so shiny as the restless ones. It looked dusty and a bit wrinkled, pushed back on a head of black hair. Cries of "Speech! Speech!" rose. All around, there suddenly was dead silence.

"Ladies and gentlemen," someone said, "I have no speech to make and no time to speak in."

You could have heard a pin drop. And yet, the easy drawl rang as familiar as folks talking at any street corner. You almost thought you had heard the voice before.

"I appear before you that I may see you," it said, "and that you may see me."

Grace felt ice-cold. It was he. His voice. He was up there on the platform. She stretched so that it hurt, but all she saw was the wrinkled stovepipe hat.

"And I'm willing to admit that, so far as the ladies are concerned, I have the best of the bargain."

Some ladies tittered.

"Though I wish it to be understood that I don't make the same acknowledgment concerning the men."

Laughter rippled, swelled, burst through the crowd. Grace laughed and clapped her hands. In back of her, an old farmer slapped his thighs and cackled, "That's telling 'em, Abe." In front of her, the lady with the slipping feathers shrieked, "Hooray for President Lincoln!"

Father caught Grace up and set her on his shoulder. Nothing but Old Glory on the roof of the car remained above the gaunt, shadowy face in the distance, and Grace thought, "My goodness, I see them—the whiskers—"

---

tittered—*giggled*
acknowledgment—*admission*
gaunt—*thin and bony*

227

He was speaking again. "I have but one question, standing here beneath the flag of our country: Will you stand by me as I stand by the flag?"

Why was the crowd so still? For an instant, Grace could see the whole figure, immensely tall, in deep black from his boots to the hat that made him look endless.

Someone shouted: "We sure will, Abe!"

The crowd took it up. Hands and hats and women's handkerchiefs rose into the air amid thundering echoes: "Yes—yes—we sure will, Abe!"

Slowly the shouting died. "I don't care for them great orators," Grace heard the farmer behind her. "I want to hear jist a plain, common feller like the rest of us, that I kin foller an' know where he's driving. Abe Lincoln fills the bill."

Grace felt herself sliding down. She was on the ground, hemmed in like a fish in a barrel. Surely it was all over, and the silent crowd was waiting only for the train to start.

Once more, she heard the voice that made you feel you had heard it all your life. "I have a little correspondent in this place," he said.

How simple it sounded! But Grace knew it could not be. She was dreaming again, as a

---

orator—*a person who makes formal speeches*

correspondent—*a person who exchanges letters with another*

moment back, when she thought
she had seen the whiskers.

"This little lady," the voice went on, "saw
from the first what great improvement might be
made in my appearance—"

It was a lovely dream. You had to keep your
eyes shut tight; if you looked, it would be time to
get up and go to school.

"—and if she is present, I would like to speak
to her. "

Grace opened her eyes wide. She was not in bed. She was in a crowd at the North East depot, unable to move, to see, to make a sound.

"Tell us the name," people shouted. "The name!"

And Mr. Lincoln replied distinctly: "Her name is Grace Bedell."

It was Father who took her hand and led her forward. She went without knowing how, without noticing that a path was opened for them. There were steps ahead, and Father gave her a boost up to the platform in sight of a thousand people, up to a pair of big, black-booted feet. Somewhere above, she heard a slow chuckle.

"She wrote me that she thought I'd look better if I wore whiskers—"

He stooped. Grace felt strong hands under her arms. Suddenly, as if she had no weight at all, she was raised high in the air, kissed on both cheeks, and gently set down again. And her cheeks burned not only from bliss but from a scratching. Up there, sprouting darkly all around the rugged face and covering cheeks and jaw, so that only the upper lip remained free, were the whiskers.

"You see, I let them grow for you, Grace," said Mr. Lincoln.

bliss—*great joy or happiness*

Grace's eyes traveled up along the black overcoat, all the way up to the whiskers and the wrinkled black hat. She could do nothing but look at the tall, gaunt, plain, familiar great man. She would have liked to stand and look forever and ever.

He took her hand. She heard him say that he hoped to see his little friend again some time; she understood that this moment had to end. He helped her down the steps and she went obediently, like a good girl, back to her proud father.

Grace's brothers, too, were suddenly there, and Mother, and Mr. Wedge, and the sour-faced Mr. Rice, and the postmaster, and Kitty, and a lot of yelling strangers. Grace saw them and did not see them. She heard cheers, yells, a shrill whistle,

231

a rumbling and puffing and screeching. But her mind heard only three words, repeated over and over: "My little friend—my little friend . . ."

Character Theme—Friendship

Thinking It Through

1. Why was Grace so excited on the morning of February 16, 1861?
2. Why could Grace see nothing but hats and a flag on the train's platform?
3. How did her father help her to see better?
4. What made Grace's cheeks burn?
5. How would you have felt if you had been able to see Abraham Lincoln?

The President [Lincoln] last night had a dream. He was in a party of plain people and as it became known who he was they began to comment on his appearance. One of them said, "He is a common-looking man." The President replied, "Common-looking people are the best in the world: that is the reason the Lord makes so many of them."
—John Hay

The Willow Basket

Carol Ryrie Brink

Carol Ryrie Brink wrote two
books about Caddie Woodlawn based
on the memories of her own grandmother, Caddie Wood-
house. Caddie was born into a hard-working pioneer
family in Wisconsin in the 1850s, and it is not hard to
see why her mother would be critical of the McCantrys,
who wanted the good things of life but did not like hard
work. If they were given another chance, though, would
the McCantrys perhaps change their ways?

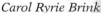

"They're shiftless—that's what they are!" said
Mrs. Woodlawn decidedly.

Shiftless was a terrible word in pioneer Wisconsin. Caddie, Tom, and Warren exchanged
discouraged glances. They had been delighted to
see the McCantrys come back—even if the father,
mother, and four children *had* returned on foot,
wheeling all of their possessions in a wheelbarrow.

Mr. and Mrs. McCantry and the four children
were standing in the road now, casting wistful
glances at the Woodlawns' cozy white house while

---

shiftless—*lazy; not having ambition*

they waited for Tom and Caddie to inform their
parents of their old neighbors' return.

"But, Mother," said Caddie, "Emma is so
nice, and all they've got left is what they can
carry in a wheelbarrow."

"They had just as good a chance here as the
rest of us," said Mrs. Woodlawn severely. "They
had a farm, but they must needs sell it for what
they could get and go on to something finer. And
now, it seems, they are back with nothing but a
wheelbarrow."

"We must not judge people too hastily, Harriet," said Mr. Woodlawn mildly, from the doorway.

"Oh, Father, we may ask them in for the night, mayn't we?" begged Caddie.

"Well, now," said Mr. Woodlawn, with a pleasant wink at Caddie over his wife's smooth dark head, "we'd better let the McCantrys go on to the next farm. The Bunns or the Silbernagles will take them in for the night, and that will let us out of any obligation."

Mrs. Woodlawn whirled about with a suspicious look in her eyes and was just in time to catch her husband's smile and the tail end of his wink.

"Go along with you!" she said, beginning to laugh. "I never intended to let them go without supper and a night's rest, and you know that. But I do feel better for having said what I think of them!"

Tom and Caddie and Warren raced away to invite the McCantrys in to supper and comfortable beds. They were a dispirited-looking lot as they sat along the roadside, waiting for the hospitality of a former neighbor. The bottom of Mrs. McCantry's dress was draggled with mud and dust, and the two boys were barefoot; but

---

obligation—*a duty*   dispirited—*dejected or sad*

Mrs. McCantry had a bonnet of the latest fashion trimmed with purple velvet pansies, and Pearly, the little girl who was next to the youngest, had a new gold ring.

Emma, the eldest of the four and Caddie's own age, slipped a warm brown arm through Caddie's and gave her a squeeze. Emma didn't have gold rings or bonnets with pansies; but she was brown and solid and comfortable, and Caddie liked her best of them all. When a bird called out in the meadow, Emma could pucker up her lips and imitate it. It was Emma who looked after the little ones as much as her mother did.

Now Mr. McCantry picked up the handles of the wheelbarrow, and Caddie thought that his shoulders looked rounder and more bent than they had when he went away. The wheelbarrow creaked as he trundled it up the path to the front door. Caddie could see that it contained some patchwork quilts and cooking utensils, a set of Mrs. McCantry's hoops, and a clock which was not running.

"Why don't you wind your clock?" asked Caddie. "I hate to see a clock that doesn't go."

"It's broke," said Emma. "We still carry it

---

trundled—*pushed*

around, but it's like most of the rest of our things. It won't work any more."

"That's too bad," said Caddie, but it gave her an idea.

Mr. and Mrs. Woodlawn met the McCantrys at the front door.

"Well, well," said Mr. Woodlawn heartily, shaking his former neighbor's hand, "so you have come back to us again, McCantry? Dunnville is a pretty good place after all."

"It is that!" said Mr. McCantry. "I'm glad to be back. We've been a weary way."

"Now, Josiah, why do you say that?" cried Mrs. McCantry sharply.

Caddie looked at her in surprise and saw that she had lost her discouraged look of a few moments ago and was quite the fine lady once again.

"We have had a most edifying journey really," she said, "and spent some months with my brother, who has a most elegant house which puts anything you have here in Dunnville quite to shame. Of course we were most elaborately entertained, and it is only by the merest chance that you see us in these circumstances. An unforeseen accident happened to our horse and carriage, and we

---

edifying—*improving to one's spiritual, intellectual, or moral character*

just thought how healthful it would be to come along on foot."

"Yes, yes, of course," said Mrs. Woodlawn hastily. "Now do come in and wash yourselves for supper."

The two little boys went along with Tom and Warren—while Pearly was taken in charge by Caddie's little sisters, Hetty and Minnie.

Caddie squeezed Emma's arm.

"Come up to my room," she said.

"Wait," said Emma, smiling mysteriously. "I've got a present for you, Caddie."

"A present for me?" Caddie was incredulous.

"It's not very good," said Emma shyly, "but I made it myself. An old lady who took us in one night, when we hadn't any money, showed me how."

She fumbled through the untidy bundle of quilts and skillets in the wheelbarrow and brought out a little willow basket.

"Why, it's ever so pretty!" cried Caddie, sincerely pleased. "But you'd ought to keep it for yourself."

---

incredulous—*unbelieving or skeptical*

"Oh, I can make lots more of them," said Emma. "Big ones, too; but we don't have room to carry them, and I thought you'd like this little one."

"I'd love it," said Caddie. "Thank you, Emma."

Meals were always good at the Woodlawns', but any sort of company rallied Mrs. Woodlawn to extra effort. Tonight, besides the supper which she had already planned, she went to the smokehouse and took down one of the hams which had come from their own well-fed pigs and had been salted and smoked under her own direction. With a sharp knife she cut the tender pink slices and fried them delicately brown before heaping them on the big blue china platter. Each slice was half ringed around with a delicate layer of fat—just enough to give variety to the lean. Mr. Woodlawn filled the plates of the hungry-looking McCantrys with the generosity of a good host, and Emma and the littler boy fell to with a will. But Pearly set up a thin wail of protest.

"I can't eat this," she said, pointing an accusing finger at the fat.

"Me neither," said Ezra, the littlest brother.

---

rallied—*roused; called together*

"You can't eat that tender bit of fat?" cried Mrs. Woodlawn in surprise.

"They've got aristocratic stomachs," Mrs. Mc-Cantry said proudly.

For a moment Mrs. Woodlawn was speechless.

"Maybe Mama could cut the fat part off for you, Pearly," began Mrs. McCantry doubtfully.

Mrs. Woodlawn's earrings began to tremble as they always did when she was excited.

"No," she said, with that gleam in her eye which her own children had learned to obey. "If you can't eat that good ham just as it is, fat and lean, you're not very hungry. My children eat what is set before them with a relish. They know if they don't they can go to bed empty. Anyone who eats at my table can do the same."

Over her tumbler of milk Caddie saw with twinkling eyes that Pearly and Ezra were eating their fat with their lean. Personally she thought the fat was the best part when it was all crisp on the outside and juicy on the inside, as Mother fried it.

The McCantrys were not there for one night only; they stayed for many days, but there were no more complaints about their meals.

---

aristocratic—*of royalty or noblity; of the best quality*   relish—*enjoyment*

Caddie and Emma enjoyed the time very much. Together they went down to the swamp where the young willows grew thickly, and the boys helped them cut slender, pliant shoots to weave more baskets. The Woodlawn land and Dr. Nightingale's land came together here at the edge of the swamp, and beyond their fences the swamp stretched away in a fairyland of tiny hummocks and islands on which grew miniature firs and tamaracks. There were wild rice in the swamp in the autumn and quantities of wild cranberries.

"What a pretty place this is!" said Emma. "If I were you, Caddie, I would build a little house on this hill overlooking the swamp. I like the nice spicy swamp smell, don't you?"

A red-winged blackbird, swaying on a reed, uttered a throaty call, and Emma answered it.

Caddie remembered this later, when she heard her father and mother talking about a home for the McCantrys.

"Really, Harriet," said Mr. Woodlawn, "I've talked alone with McCantry, and they have reached rock bottom. He hasn't any money left."

"To hear *her* talk, you would think they were millionaires."

---

pliant—*flexible; easily bent*
hummocks—*small hills or mounds of earth*

tamaracks—*trees having short needles that fall off in the autumn*

"I know, my dear, but she's a foolish woman. It's her foolishness that's brought them where they are, I think. But we can't let them starve for all that, and we can't have them living with us always either. Somehow we've got to set them on their feet once more."

"Well, Johnny, grumble as I may, I suppose that you are always right about such things. What had we better do?" sighed Mrs. Woodlawn.

"I thought we might give them a little land at the edge of our place somewhere. Perhaps one of our neighbors on the other side would contribute a little, too, and then all of the neighbors could get together and help build them a house. We could make a sort of raising bee out of it."

"A raising bee!" repeated Mrs. Woodlawn, her eyes beginning to shine. "Yes, we could do that."

"Oh, Father," cried Caddie, forgetting that she had not been included in the conversation so far, "that would be lots of fun! And I'll tell you the very place for the house."

"You will?" laughed her father. "So you've already picked the site?"

"Yes, I have! It's that corner down by the swamp. Emma loves the smell and the redwing

---

contribute—*to give; to share*
raising bee—*a gathering of neighbors to build a house*

blackbirds, and they could get all the cranberries and wild rice they needed and maybe they could sell what they didn't need, and they could make willow baskets out of the willow shoots and sell those too."

"Willow baskets?" asked her father. "Sell willow baskets? You're going a little too fast for me, daughter. I'm lost in the swamp."

"Oh, wait!" cried Caddie. She was in one of her eager moods when ideas came too fast to be expressed. She flew out of the room and returned in a moment with Emma's basket in her hands. "Look! Wouldn't you pay money for a big basket, if it were as nicely made as that?"

Her mother took the basket in her own slender hands and looked it over carefully. "Yes, I would," she said. "I believe a lot of people would. We've never had anyone around here who could make baskets."

"Well, we have now," said Caddie. "Can't we set the McCantrys up in business?"

"Where's my bonnet?" cried Mrs. Woodlawn. "I'm going to call on the neighbors!"

Dancing with excitement, Caddie ran for her mother's tasteful gray bonnet.

"Thank Kind Providence, it doesn't have purple pansies on it," said Mrs. Woodlawn as she went to the barn for a horse.

There was nothing like another's need to rally the pioneers of that day. Dr. Nightingale joined Mr. Woodlawn in donating a good-sized strip of land at the edge of the swamp. Another man, who had plenty of timber on his farm, offered enough logs to build a cabin if others would cut and haul them. Men and boys who had nothing to give but their time gladly did the cutting and hauling. One neighbor offered a pig, another a cow, and a third the use of his horse and plow to break a garden spot.

On the day of the "raising," men and boys on horseback arrived early from all the country around and went to work on the cabin. The women and girls came along later in the morning with covered dishes and jars of pickles and preserves.

Mrs. Woodlawn and Mrs. McCantry, with the help of the children, had made tables by putting long planks on sawhorses near the site of the new house. Over an open fire were great pots of coffee

244

and stone jars full of Mrs. Woodlawn's choice baked beans.

It was not often that the neighbors came together for a common purpose. They were a settled community now, and it had been a long time since one of them had had a raising for himself. There had been the time of the Indian "Massacree Scare," when they had all come together under the Woodlawns' roof for several days; but then they had been filled with fear and distrust. Now they came together in a spirit of friendship and helpfulness.

The children raced about playing tag and "Blindman's Buff" and "I Spy," while the men laid up stones for a fireplace and hewed and raised the logs one upon another to make the Mc-Cantrys' walls. The women unpacked baskets and laughed and chattered as they spread the feast. They were seeing friends and neighbors they had not seen for weeks, perhaps for months or years.

There was one thing which Mrs. Woodlawn and Mrs. McCantry had in common: they both loved a party. With happy, flushed faces they moved about among the neighbors, shaking hands, filling coffee cups, and urging more beans or gingerbread on people who had already eaten their fill.

The swamp echoed with the ringing of axes and mallets and the cries of men as they heaved the upper logs into place. By sundown the Mc-Cantrys had a house of their own. All the hard work was done and only the finishing was left for Mr. McCantry. As the neighbors prepared to depart, other gifts came out of their wagons: a sack of potatoes, a rocking chair, a bushel of turnips, a goosefeather pillow, strings of dried apples, a couple of live chickens.

At the last moment Mr. Woodlawn nailed up a shelf by the new fireplace. No one knew why until Caddie and Emma came breathlessly over the fields from the Woodlawns' house carrying the McCantry's clock. Caddie and her father had sat up late in the attic shop the night before to take it all apart, clean it, and coax it to run. Now it ticked away on the shelf as brightly as a cricket.

"There!" said Caddie triumphantly. "A house is ready to live in when a clock is ticking in it!"

"My land!" said Mrs. McCantry. "That clock hasn't ticked for years—just like us, I guess." Her bonnet was all crooked with excitement and the purple pansies bobbed and trembled over one ear, but for once her eyes were perfectly frank and honest. "I know what you've been thinking of us,

mallets—*hammers*

246

Mrs. Woodlawn," she said slowly. "Shiftless, you thought, and I guess you were right. But we've seen what neighbors can be like today. We're going to set right out to be good neighbors ourselves. You won't ever regret all that you have done for us!"

The two women looked at each other and for the first time they smiled in sudden understanding. Caddie and Emma smiled at each other, too, and hugged each other.

Caddie knew that Mrs. McCantry might often forget her good resolutions, for she was that kind of person; but she knew also that Emma would always make up for Mrs. McCantry's shortcomings, for Emma was a person to trust.

The McCantrys would be good neighbors.

---

resolutions—*decision to do something*

Character Theme—Compassion, Friendship, & Kindness

Thinking It Through

1. What family had returned with all their belongings in a wheelbarrow?
2. What gift did Emma give Caddie?
3. What rule did Mrs. Woodlawn have for her children at the table?
4. In your opinion, where had the two youngest McCantry children learned to be ungrateful?
5. What was Caddie's idea to help the McCantrys make some money?

My Daily Creed

Let me be a little kinder,
Let me be a little blinder
To the faults of those about me;
Let me praise a little more;
Let me be, when I am weary,
Just a little bit more cheery;
Let me serve a little better
Those that I am striving for.

Let me be a little braver
When temptation bids me waver;
Let me strive a little harder
To be all that I should be;
Let me be a little meeker
With the brother that is weaker;
Let me think more of my neighbor
And a little less of me.

—*Author Unknown*

strive—*to put forth great effort*
bids—*invites; asks*

waver—*to go back and forth;*
to seem unsure

God's Trees

Helen Frazee Bower

Far away on a hillside grew a forest of trees. Little and big, old and young, tall and short, all grew together. The trees were happy with life just as it was on the hillside. They loved the warm sunlight of summer, spring's cool, silvery rains, the gorgeous reds and golds of autumn, and winter's blanket of glistening snow. But sometimes they spoke of the future, of the things they would like to do and be when they grew up.

One said, "You know, I should like to be a baby's cradle. I have seen people come into this forest carrying babies in their arms. I think a baby is the sweetest thing I have ever seen, and I should like to be made into a baby's bed."

A second tree spoke. "That would not please me at all. I want to be something important. I would like to be a great ship, strong and stately. I would like to cross many waters and carry cargoes of gold, silver, and precious jewels."

---

glistening—*shining with reflected light*
stately—*dignified; majestic; worthy of honor*

One little tree stood off by himself, apparently in deep reflection, but he did not speak.

"And what would you like to be?" asked the Mother Tree. "Have you no dreams for the future?"

"No dreams," he answered, "except to stand on a hillside and point to God. What could a tree do that is better than that?"

Mother Tree looked at him fondly. "What, indeed?" she said.

Years passed. The trees grew up. One day men came to the forest and cut down the first little tree.

"I wonder whether I shall be made into a baby's cradle now. I hope so. I have waited so long," he whispered.

But the little tree was not made into a cradle. Instead, it was hewn into rough pieces and carelessly put together to form a manger in a stable in Bethlehem. He was heartbroken. "I do not like this at all," he wailed. "This is not what I planned—to be shoved into this dark cave (for that is what the stable really was), with no one to see me but the cattle."

---

apparently—*seemingly*   hewn—*chopped*
reflection—*serious thought*

But God, who loves little trees, whispered, "Wait, I will show you something." And He did. For—

There were in the same country shepherds abiding in the field, keeping watch over their flocks by night. And, lo, the angel of the Lord came upon them, and the glory of the Lord shone round about them: and they were sore afraid.

And the angel said unto them, Fear not: for, behold, I bring you good tidings of great joy, which shall be to all people. For unto you is born this day in the city of David a Savior, which is Christ the Lord. And this shall be a sign unto you; Ye shall find the babe wrapped in swaddling clothes, lying in a manger.

And suddenly there was with the angel a multitude of the heavenly host praising God, and saying, Glory to God in the highest, and on earth peace, good will toward men.

And it came to pass, as the angels were gone away from them into heaven, the shepherds said one to another, Let us now go even unto Bethlehem, and see this thing which is come to pass, which the Lord hath made known unto us. And they came with haste, and found Mary, and Joseph, and the babe lying in a manger.

---

sore—*greatly*

In the stillness of the night God had laid there
His own Babe—the Son of God. The manger
quivered with delight. "Oh, this is wonderful!" he
whispered. "In all my dreams I never thought to
hold a Baby like this. This is better than all my
planning. Why, I am part of a miracle!"

And out on the hillside, the trees of the forest clapped their hands, because their brother, the
little manger, had seen his wish come true.

Years passed by, and men came to the forest
to cut down the second tree. "I wonder whether
I shall be made into a great vessel now," this one
thought. "I have waited so long. Now, perhaps, I
shall do great things of which I have dreamed."

---

quivered—*trembled*

But the little tree did not do great things. He was not made into a great vessel, but instead he became a tiny fishing boat, owned by a simple Galilean fisherman named Peter. The little boat was most unhappy. One day he stood by the shores of the Sea of Galilee and pondered, while Peter washed his nets.

"To think that my life has come to this!" he said. "Just a fishing boat! And Peter is not even a good fisherman."

But God, who loves little trees, said, "Wait, I will show you something." And He did. For—

Out from the crowd came a Person called Jesus, who entered into the little boat and taught the people. He spoke words of such wisdom, beauty,

and light that the multitude, and even the little fishing boat, listened eagerly. When He had finished, He told Peter to launch out into the deep and let down his nets again. And there were so many fish that the net broke!

The little boat trembled, not so much with the weight of fishes as with the weight of wonder in his heart. "This is wonderful!" he whispered. "In all my dreams I never thought to carry a cargo like this; why, I am a part of a miracle. This is better than all my planning."

And out on the hillside, all the trees of the forest clapped their hands because their brother, the boat, had known fulfillment.

Months went by, and men came to the forest to cut down the third little tree—the one that had wanted just to stand on a hill and point to God. He was most unhappy. "I do not want to go into the valley," he thought. "Why couldn't men just leave me alone?"

But men did not leave the little tree alone. They tore away its branches; they cut into its bark, and deeper, into its very heart. They hewed it apart and put it together again in the form of a crude cross. The little tree quivered through all its being.

launch out—*to put to sea*   crude—*rough*
fulfillment—*satisfaction of one's desires*

"This is terrible!" it whispered. "They are going to hang someone. Oh, I never wanted this to happen to me—I who only wanted to point to God! This is awful."

But God, who loves little trees, said, "Wait, I will show you something." And He did. For—

One day, outside Jerusalem, a great multitude gathered. In their midst was Jesus, and beside Him was the cross.

> And as they led him away, they laid hold upon one Simon, a Cyrenian, coming out of the country, and on him they laid the cross, that he might bear it after Jesus. . . . And when they were come to the place which is called Calvary, there they crucified him. . . .

The cross shuddered beneath its weight of agony and shame. Then suddenly a miracle happened.

> Jesus, when he had cried again with a loud voice, yielded up the ghost. And, behold, the veil of the temple was rent in twain from the top to the bottom; and the earth did quake, and the rocks were rent. . . . Now when the centurion, and they that were with him, watching Jesus, saw the earthquake, and those things that were done, they feared greatly, saying, Truly this was the Son of God.

Cyrenian—*a person from Cyrene in northern Africa*
agony—*very great pain*

rent—*torn*
centurion—*a commander of 100 soldiers*

The little tree that had become a cross heard, floating down from the heavenly places, the echo of a remembered promise: "Now is the judgment of this world: now shall the prince of this world be cast out. And I, if I be lifted up from the earth, will draw all men unto me."

And the cross began to understand.

"This is wonderful!" he whispered. "I am part of a miracle. In all my dreams I never thought to point to God in this way. This is better than all my planning."

And so it was. For hundreds of trees have stood on the hillslopes through the years, but not one of them has ever been able to point a man to God. Only the cross of Calvary can do that.

And out on the hillside all the trees of the forest bowed their heads and thanked God, because their brother, the cross, had known fulfillment.

Character Theme—Contentment

Thinking It Through

1. What became of the first tree in the forest?
2. What kind of vessel did the second tree become?
3. Why did the fishing boat feel that he was part of a miracle?
4. How did the third tree point to God?

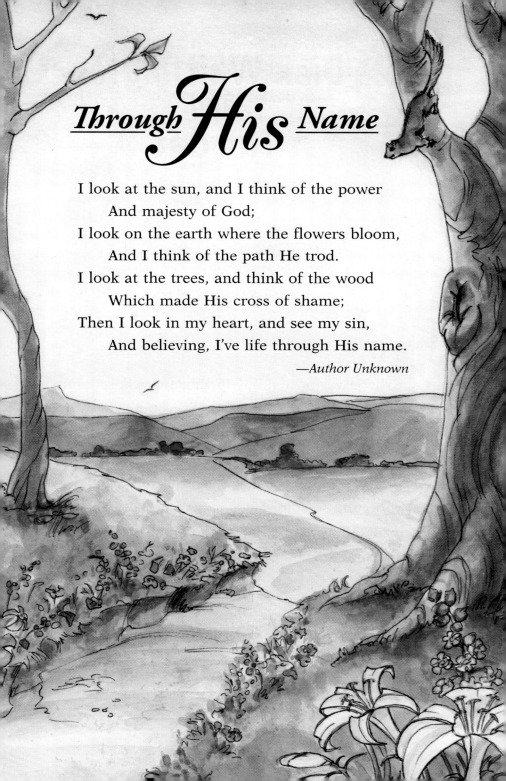

Through His Name

I look at the sun, and I think of the power
    And majesty of God;
I look on the earth where the flowers bloom,
    And I think of the path He trod.
I look at the trees, and think of the wood
    Which made His cross of shame;
Then I look in my heart, and see my sin,
    And believing, I've life through His name.

—*Author Unknown*

Dick Whittington and His Cat

an old story of England
retold by
James Baldwin

Dick Whittington was a real boy who was born in the 1300s, and he really did become Lord Mayor of London. For hundreds of years people have liked to think that this story about his cat is true, too.

There was once a boy in England whose name was Richard Whittington, but everybody called him Dick. His father and mother had died when he was only a baby, and the people who took care of him were very poor. Dick was not old enough to work, and so sometimes he had no breakfast, and sometimes he had no dinner, and he was glad at any time to get a crust of bread or a drop of milk.

Now, in the town where Dick lived, the people liked to talk about the big city of London. None of them had ever been there, but they seemed to know all about the wonderful things which were

London—*the capital of England*

to be seen there. "The folks who live in London are fine gentlemen and ladies," they said. "There is singing and music there all day long. Nobody is ever hungry there, and nobody has to work, because the streets are all paved with gold."

Dick listened to these stories and wished that he could go to London.

One day a big wagon drawn by eight horses, all with bells on their heads, drove into the little town. Dick saw the wagon standing by the inn, and he thought that it must be going to the fine city of London.

When the driver came out and was ready to start, the lad ran up and asked him if he might walk by the side of the wagon. The driver asked him some questions, and when he learned how poor Dick was and that he had neither father nor mother, he told him that he might do as he liked.

It was a long walk for the little lad, but by and by he came to the city of London. He ran as fast as he could from one street to another, trying to find those that were paved with gold. He had once seen a piece of money that was gold, and knew that it would buy a great many things, and now he thought that if he could get only a little bit of the pavement, he would have everything he wanted.

Poor Dick ran till he was so tired that he could run no farther. It was growing dark, and in every street there was only dirt instead of gold. He sat down in a dark corner and cried himself to sleep.

When he woke up the next morning, he was very hungry, but there was not even a crust of bread for him to eat. He forgot all about the golden pavements and thought only of food. He walked about from one street to another and at last grew so hungry that he began to ask those whom he met to give him a penny to buy something to eat.

"Go to work, you idle fellow," said some of them; and the rest passed him by without even looking at him.

"I wish I *could* go to work!" said Dick.

By and by Dick grew so tired and weak that he could go no farther. He sat down by the door of a fine house and wished that he was back again in the little town where he was born.

The cook, who was just getting dinner, saw him, and called out, "What are you doing there, you little beggar? If you don't get away quick, I'll throw a pan of hot dishwater over you. Then I guess you will jump."

---

idle—*lazy; avoiding work*

Just at that time the master of the house, whose name was Mr. Fitzwarren, came home to dinner. When he saw the ragged little fellow at his door, he said, "My lad, what are you doing here? I am afraid you are a lazy fellow and that you want to live without work."

"No, indeed!" said Dick. "I would like to work, if I could find anything to do. But I do not know anybody in this town, and I have not had anything to eat for a long time."

"Poor little fellow!" said Mr. Fitzwarren. "Come in, and I will see what I can do for you." And he ordered the cook to give the lad a good dinner and then to find some light work for him to do.

Little Dick would have been very happy in his new home if it had not been for the cross cook. She would often say, "You are my boy now, and so you must do as I tell you. Look sharp there! Make the fires, carry out the ashes, wash these dishes, sweep the floor, bring in the wood! Oh, what a lazy fellow you are!" And then she would box his ears or beat him with the broomstick.

At last, little Alice, his master's daughter, saw how he was treated, and she told the cook she would be fired if she was not kinder to the lad. After that, Dick had an easier time of it, but his troubles were not over yet, by any means.

His bed was in an attic at the top of the house, far away from the rooms where the other people slept. There were many holes in the floor and walls, and every night a great number of rats and mice came in. They tormented Dick so much that he did not know what to do.

One day a gentleman gave him a penny for cleaning his shoes, and he made up his mind that he would buy a cat with it. The very next morning, he met a girl who was carrying a cat in her arms.

"I will give you a penny for that cat," Dick said.

"All right," the girl said. "You may have her, and you will find that she is a good mouser, too."

tormented—*caused great pain and trouble*
mouser—*a catcher of mice*

264

Dick hid his cat in the attic, and every day he carried a part of his dinner to her. It was not long before she had driven all the rats and mice away, and then Dick could sleep soundly every night.

The Cat Who Went to Sea

Some time after that, a ship that belonged to Mr. Fitzwarren was about to start on a voyage across the sea. It was loaded with goods that were to be sold in lands far away. Mr. Fitzwarren wanted to give his servants a chance for good fortune, too, and so he called all of them into the parlor and asked if they had anything they would like to send out in the ship for trade.

Everyone had something to send—everyone but Dick; and as he had neither money nor goods, he stayed in the kitchen and did not come in with the rest. Little Alice guessed why he did not come, and so she said to her papa, "Poor Dick ought to have a chance, too. Here is some money out of my own purse that you may put in for him."

"No, no, my child!" said Mr. Fitzwarren. "He must risk something of his own." And then he called very loudly, "Here, Dick! What are you going to send out on the ship?"

voyage—*a long trip by ship*
parlor—*a living room*

Dick heard him and came into the room.

"I have nothing in the world," he said, "but a cat which I bought some time ago for a penny."

"Fetch your cat, then, my lad," said Mr. Fitzwarren, "and let her go out. Who knows but that she will bring you some profit?"

Dick, with tears in his eyes, carried his only possession down to the ship and gave her to the captain. Everybody laughed at him, but little Alice felt sorry for him and gave him money to buy another cat.

After that, the cook was worse than before. She made fun of him for sending his cat to sea. "Do you think," she would say, "that cat will sell for enough money to buy a stick to beat you?"

At last Dick could not stand her abuse any longer, and he made up his mind to go back to his old home in the little country town. So, very early in the morning, he started. He walked as far as the place called Holloway, and there he sat down on a stone, which to this day is called Whittington's Stone.

As he sat there very sad, and wondering which way he should go, he heard the bells on Bow Church, far away, ringing out a merry chime. He listened. They seemed to say to him,

---

profit—*good; benefit; the money left after all costs are covered*

Turn again, Whittington,
Thrice Lord Mayor of London.

"Well, well!" he said to himself. "I would put up with almost anything to be Lord Mayor of London when I am a man, and to ride in a fine coach! I think I will go back and let the old cook cuff and scold as much as she pleases."

Dick did go back, and he was able to get into the kitchen and set about his work before the cook came downstairs to get breakfast.

Mr. Fitzwarren's ship made a long voyage and at last reached a strange land on the other side of the sea. The people had never seen any Englishmen before, and they came in great crowds to buy the fine things with which the ship was loaded. The captain wanted very much to trade with the king of the country, and it was not long before the king sent word for him to come to the palace and see him.

The captain did so. He was shown into a beautiful room and given a seat on a rich carpet all flowered with silver and gold. The king and queen were seated not far away, and soon a number of dishes were brought in for dinner.

They had hardly begun to eat when an army of rats and mice rushed in and devoured all the meat before anyone could hinder them. The captain

---

cuff—*to hit with an open hand; slap*
hinder—*to slow or stop progress*

wondered at this. "Isn't it unpleasant to have so many rats and mice about?" he asked, as politely as he could.

"Oh, yes!" was the answer. "It is indeed unpleasant, and the king would give half his treasure if he could get rid of them."

The captain jumped for joy. He remembered the cat which little Whittington had sent out, and he told the king that he had a little creature on board his ship which would make short work of the pests.

Then it was the king's turn to jump for joy, and he jumped so high that his yellow cap, or turban, dropped off his head.

"Bring the creature to me," he said. "If she will do what you say, I will load your ship with gold."

The captain went down to the ship to get the cat while the king and queen made haste to have another dinner made ready.

The captain, with Dick's cat under his arm, reached the palace just in time to see the table crowded with rats. The cat leaped out upon them, and oh! what havoc she did make among the troublesome creatures! Most of them were soon stretched dead upon the floor, while the rest

havoc—*great destruction*

scampered away to their holes and did not dare to come out again.

The king had never been so glad in his life, and the queen asked that the creature that had done such wonders should be brought to her. The captain called, "Kitty, kitty, kitty!" and the cat came up and rubbed against his legs. He picked her up and offered her to the queen, who at first was afraid to touch her.

However, the captain stroked the cat and called, "Kitty, kitty, kitty!" and then the queen ventured to touch her. The captain then put the cat down on the queen's lap, where she purred and purred until she went to sleep.

The king at once made a bargain with the captain for all the goods on board the ship, and then he gave him ten times as much for the cat as all the rest came to.

The captain was very glad. He bade the king and queen good-bye, and the very next day he set sail for England.

Good Tidings

One morning, Mr. Fitzwarren was sitting at his desk in his office. Hearing someone tap softly at his door, he said, "Who's there?'"

"A friend," was the answer. "I have come to bring you news of your ship."

Mr. Fitzwarren jumped up quickly and opened the door. Whom should he see waiting there but the captain, with a heavy box of jewels in his hands! Mr. Fitzwarren was so full of joy that he lifted up his eyes and thanked God for sending him such good fortune.

The captain soon told the story of the cat, and then he showed the rich present that the king and queen had sent to Dick in payment for her. As soon as the good gentleman heard this, he called out to his servants,

> Go send him in, and tell him of his fame;
> Pray call him Mr. Whittington by name.

Some of the men who stood by said that such a great fortune ought not to be given to a boy; but Mr. Fitzwarren frowned upon them.

"It is his own," he said, "and I will not hold back one penny from him."

Dick was scouring the pots when word was brought to him that he should go to the office. "Oh, I am so dirty!" he said, "and my shoes all scuffed and worn." But he was told to make haste.

Mr. Fitzwarren ordered a chair to be set for him, and then the lad began to think that they were making fun of him. "I beg that you won't

---

scouring—*scrubbing clean*

play tricks with a poor boy like me," he said. "Please let me go back to my work."

"Mr. Whittington," said Mr. Fitzwarren, "this is no joke at all. The captain has sold your cat and has brought you, in return for her, more riches than I have in the whole world." Then he opened the box of jewels and showed Dick his treasures.

The poor boy did not know what to do. He begged his master to take part of it, but Mr. Fitzwarren said, "No, it is all your own, and I feel sure that you will make good use of it."

Dick then offered some of his jewels to little Alice and her mother. They thanked him and told him that they felt great joy at his good fortune but wanted him to keep his riches for himself.

But he was too kindhearted to keep everything for himself. He gave nice presents to the

captain and the sailors and to the servants in Mr.
Fitzwarren's house. He even remembered the
cross old cook.

After that, Whittington's face was washed and
his hair cut, and he was dressed in a nice suit of
clothes. Then he was as handsome a young man
as ever walked the streets of London.

Some years after that, there was a fine wed-
ding at the finest church in London, and Miss
Alice became the wife of Mr. Richard Whittington.
The lord mayor was there, and the great judges,
and the sheriffs, and many rich merchants; and
everybody was very happy.

And Richard Whittington
became a great merchant and
was one of the foremost men
in London. He was sheriff
of the city, and thrice lord
mayor, and King Henry V
made him a knight.

He built the
famous prison of
Newgate in London.
On the archway in
front of the prison

foremost—*leading;
most important*

was a statue carved in stone of Sir Richard Whittington and his cat; and for hundreds of years this statue was shown to all who visited London.

Character Theme—Forgiveness & Kindness

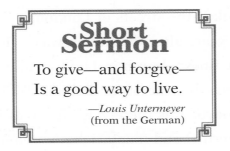

Short Sermon

To give—and forgive—
Is a good way to live.

—*Louis Untermeyer*
(from the German)

Thinking It Through

1. Who gave Dick food, work, and a place to live in London?

2. How was Dick treated at the Fitzwarren home?

3. Why did Dick buy a cat?

4. Why was Dick's cat so valuable to the king and queen?

5. How does the "Short Sermon" at the end of the story apply to Dick?

Cats

Cats sleep
Anywhere,
Any table,
Any chair,
Top of piano,
Window-ledge,
In the middle,
On the edge,
Open drawer,
Empty shoe,
Anybody's
Lap will do,
Fitted in a
Cardboard box,
In the cupboard
With your frocks—
Anywhere!
They don't care!
Cats sleep
Anywhere.

—*Eleanor Farjeon*

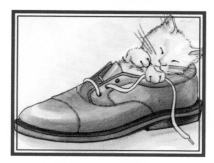

frocks—*dresses; smocks*

Cat

The black cat yawns,
Open her jaws,
Stretches her legs,
And shows her claws.

Then she gets up
And stands on four
Long stiff legs
And yawns some more.

She shows her sharp teeth,
She stretches her lip,
Her slice of a tongue
Turns up at the tip.

Lifting herself
On her delicate toes,
She arches her back
As high as it goes.

She lets herself down
With particular care,
And pads away
With her tail in the air.

—*Mary Britton Miller*

delicate—*soft or light; easily broken*

276

The Elephant's Child

Rudyard Kipling

We know, of course, how the elephant got his long trunk, how the camel got his hump, and how the rhinoceros got his baggy skin—God made them that way. It is fun, though, to read the humorous explanations Rudyard Kipling gives in his famous book, *Just So Stories*.

In the High and Far-Off Times the Elephant, O Best Beloved, had no trunk. He had only a blackish, bulgy nose, as big as a boot, that he could wriggle about from side to side; but he couldn't pick up things with it. But there was one Elephant—a new Elephant—an Elephant's Child— who was full of 'satiable curtiosity, and that means he asked ever so many questions. And he lived in Africa, and he filled all Africa with his 'satiable curtiosities.

He asked his tall aunt, the Ostrich, why her tail-feathers grew just so, and his tall aunt, the Ostrich, popped him with her hard claw. He asked

---

'satiable curtiosity—*insatiable curiosity, or curiosity that can never be satisfied* his tall uncle, the Giraffe, what made his skin spotty, and his tall uncle, the Giraffe, popped him with his hard hoof. And still he was full of 'satiable curtiosity! He asked his broad aunt, the Hippopotamus, why her eyes were red, and his broad aunt, the Hippopotamus, popped him with her broad hoof; and he asked his hairy uncle, the Baboon, why melons tasted just so, and his hairy uncle, the Baboon, popped him with his hairy paw. And *still* he was full of 'satiable curtiosity! He asked questions about everything that he saw, or heard, or felt, or smelt, or touched, and all his uncles and his aunts popped him. And still he was full of 'satiable curtiosity!

One fine morning, this 'satiable Elephant's Child asked a new fine question that he had never asked before. He asked, "What does the Crocodile have for dinner?" Then everybody said, "Hush!" in a loud and dreadful tone, and they popped him immediately and directly.

By and by, when that was finished, he came upon Kolokolo Bird sitting in the middle of a wait-a-bit thorn-bush, and he said, "My father has popped me, and my mother has popped me; all my aunts and uncles have popped me for my 'satiable curtiosity; and still I want to know what the Crocodile has for dinner!"

Then Kolokolo Bird said, with a mournful cry, "Go to the banks of the great gray-green, greasy Limpopo River, all set about with fever-trees, and find out."

That very next morning, this 'satiable Elephant's Child took a hundred pounds of bananas, and a hundred pounds of sugar-cane, and seventeen melons, and said to all his dear families, "Good-bye. I am going to the great gray-green, greasy Limpopo River, all set about with fever-trees, to find out what the Crocodile has for dinner."

He went from Graham's Town to Kimberley, and from Kimberley to Khama's Country, and from Khama's Country he went east by north, eating melons all the time, till at last he came to the banks of the great gray-green, greasy Limpopo River, all set about with fever-trees, precisely as Kolokolo Bird had said.

Now you must know and understand, O Best Beloved, that till that very week, and day, and hour, and minute, this 'satiable Elephant's Child had never seen a Crocodile, and did not know what one was like. It was all his 'satiable curtiosity.

The first thing that he found was a Bi-Colored-Python-Rock-Snake curled round a rock.

mournful—*sad; sorrowful*

"'Scuse me," said the Elephant's Child most politely, "but have you seen such a thing as a Crocodile in these parts?"

"*Have* I seen a Crocodile?" said the Bi-Colored-Python-Rock-Snake, in a voice of dreadful scorn. "What will you ask me next?"

"'Scuse me," said the Elephant's Child, "but could you kindly tell me what he has for dinner?"

Then the Bi-Colored-Python-Rock-Snake uncoiled himself very quickly from the rock, and popped the Elephant's Child with his scalesome, flailsome tail.

So he said good-bye very politely to the Bi-Colored-Python-Rock-Snake, and helped to coil him up on the rock again, and went on, a little warm, but not at all astonished, eating melons, and throwing the rinds about, because he could not pick them up, till he trod on what he thought was a log of wood at the very edge of the great gray-green, greasy Limpopo River, all set about with fever-trees.

But it was really the Crocodile, O Best Beloved, and the Crocodile winked one eye—like this!

"'Scuse me," said the Elephant's Child most politely, "but do you happen to have seen a Crocodile in these parts?"

---

trod—*walked*

Then the Crocodile winked the other eye, and lifted half his tail out of the mud; and the Elephant's Child stepped back most politely, because he did not wish to be popped again.

"Come hither, Little One," said the Crocodile. "Why do you ask such things?"

"'Scuse me," said the Elephant's Child most politely, "but my father has popped me, my mother has popped me, not to mention my tall aunt, the Ostrich, and my tall uncle, the Giraffe, as well as my broad aunt, the Hippopotamus, and my hairy uncle, the Baboon, *and* including the Bi-Colored-Python-Rock-Snake, with the scalesome, flailsome tail, just up the bank, and *so*, if it's quite all the same to you, I don't want to be popped any more."

"Come hither, Little One," said the Crocodile, "for I am the Crocodile," and he wept crocodile tears to show it was quite true.

Then the Elephant's Child grew all breathless, and panted, and kneeled down on the bank and said, "You are the very person I have been looking for all these long days. Will you please tell me what you have for dinner?"

"Come hither, Little One," said the Crocodile, "and I'll whisper."

Then the Elephant's Child put his head down

hither—*here*   crocodile tears—*insincere tears*

close to the Crocodile's musky, tusky mouth, and the Crocodile caught him by his little nose, which up to that very week, day, hour, and minute, had been no bigger than a boot, though much more useful.

"I think," said the Crocodile—and he said it between his teeth, like this—"I think today I will begin with Elephant's Child!"

At this, O Best Beloved, the Elephant's Child was much annoyed, and he said, speaking through his nose, like this, "Led go! You are hurtig be!"

Then the Elephant's Child sat back on his little haunches, and pulled, and pulled, and pulled, and his nose began to stretch. And the Crocodile floundered into the water, making it all creamy

with great sweeps of his tail, and *he* pulled, and pulled, and pulled.

And the Elephant's Child's nose kept on stretching; and the Elephant's Child spread all his little four legs and pulled, and pulled, and pulled, and his nose kept on stretching; and the Crocodile threshed his tail like an oar, and *he* pulled, and pulled, and pulled, and at each pull the Elephant's Child's nose grew longer and longer!

Then the Elephant's Child felt his legs slipping, and he said through his nose, which was now nearly five feet long, "This is too butch for be!"

Then the Bi-Colored-Python-Rock-Snake came down from the bank, and knotted himself in a

flounder—*to struggle awkwardly to move*

double-clove-hitch round the Elephant's Child's hind legs, and he pulled, and the Elephant's Child pulled, and the Crocodile pulled; but the Elephant's Child and the Bi-Colored-Python-Rock-Snake pulled hardest; and at last the Crocodile let go of the Elephant's Child's nose with a plop that you could hear all up and down the Limpopo.

Then the Elephant's Child sat down most hard and sudden; but first he was careful to say "Thank you" to the Bi-Colored-Python-Rock-Snake; and next he was kind to his poor pulled nose, and wrapped it all up in cool banana leaves, and hung it in the great gray-green, greasy Limpopo to cool.

"What are you doing that for?" said the Bi-Colored-Python-Rock-Snake.

"'Scuse me," said the Elephant's Child, "but my nose is badly out of shape, and I am waiting for it to shrink."

"Then you will have to wait a long time," said the Bi-Colored-Python-Rock-Snake. "Some people do not know what is good for them."

The Elephant's Child sat there for three days waiting for his nose to shrink. But it never grew any shorter, and, besides, it made him squint. For, O Best Beloved, you will see and understand

---

double-clove-hitch—*a kind of knot for fastening a rope around a pole*

squint—*to look with partly closed eyes*

that the Crocodile had pulled it out into a really truly trunk same as all Elephants have today.

At the end of the third day a fly came and stung him on the shoulder, and before he knew what he was doing, he lifted up his trunk and hit that fly dead with the end of it.

"'Vantage number one!" said the Bi-Colored-Python-Rock-Snake. "You couldn't have done that with a mere-smear nose. Try and eat a little now."

Before he thought what he was doing, the Elephant's Child put out his trunk and plucked a large bundle of grass, dusted it clean against his forelegs, and stuffed it into his own mouth.

"'Vantage number two!" said the Bi-Colored-Python-Rock-Snake. "You couldn't have done that with a mere-smear nose. Don't you think the sun is very hot here?"

"It is," said the Elephant's Child, and before he thought what he was doing, he schlooped up a schloop of mud from the banks of the great gray-green, greasy Limpopo, and slapped it on his head, where it made a cool schloopy-sloshy mud-cap all trickly behind his ears.

"'Vantage number three!" said the Bi-Colored-Python-Rock-Snake. "You couldn't have done that with a mere-smear nose. Now how do you feel about being popped again?"

"'Scuse me," said the Elephant's Child, "but I should not like it at all."

"How would you like to pop somebody?" said the Bi-Colored-Python-Rock-Snake.

"I should like it very much indeed," said the Elephant's Child.

"Well," said the Bi-Colored-Python-Rock-Snake, "you will find that new nose of yours very useful to pop people with."

"Thank you," said the Elephant's Child, "I'll remember that; and now I think I'll go home to all my dear families and try."

So the Elephant's Child went home across Africa, frisking and whisking his trunk. When he wanted fruit to eat, he pulled fruit down from a tree, instead of waiting for it to fall as he used to do. When he wanted grass, he plucked grass up from the ground, instead of going on his knees as he used to do. When the flies bit him, he broke off the branch of a tree and used it as a fly-whisk; and he made himself a new, cool, slushy-squshy mud-cap whenever the sun was hot. When he felt lonely walking through Africa, he sang to himself down his trunk, and the noise was louder than several brass bands.

He went especially out of his way to find a broad Hippopotamus (she was no relation of his),

and he popped her to make sure that the Bi-Colored-Python-Rock-Snake had spoken the truth about his new trunk. The rest of the time he picked up the melon rinds that he had dropped on his way to the Limpopo—for he was a Tidy Pachyderm.

One dark evening he came back to all his dear families, and he coiled up his trunk and said, "How do you do?"

They were very glad to see him, and immediately said, "Come here and be popped for your 'satiable curtiosity."

"Pooh," said the Elephant's Child. "I don't think you peoples know anything about popping; but *I* do, and I'll show you."

---

pachyderm (păk′ĭ·dûrm)—*a large, thick-skinned, hoofed animal, such as an elephant, rhinoceros, or hippopotamus*

Then he uncurled his trunk and knocked two of his dear brothers head over heels.

"Where did you learn that trick, and what have you done to your nose?" said they.

"I got a new one from the Crocodile on the banks of the great gray-green, greasy Limpopo River," said the Elephant's Child. "I asked him what he had for dinner, and he gave me this to keep."

"It looks very ugly," said his hairy uncle, the Baboon.

"It does," said the Elephant's Child. "But it's very useful," and he picked up his hairy uncle, the Baboon, by one hairy leg, and plunked him into a bird's nest.

Then that bad Elephant's Child popped all his dear families till they were greatly astonished. He pulled out one of his tall Ostrich aunt's tail-feathers; and he caught his tall uncle, the Giraffe, by the hind leg, and dragged him through a bush; and he shouted at his broad aunt, the Hippopotamus, and blew bubbles into her ear when she was sleeping in the water after meals; but he never let anyone touch Kolokolo Bird.

At last, things grew so exciting that his dear families went off one by one in a hurry to the banks of the great gray-green, greasy Limpopo

River, all set about with fever-trees, to borrow new noses from the Crocodile. When they came back, nobody popped anybody any more; and ever since that day, O Best Beloved, all the Elephants you will ever see, besides all those that you won't, have trunks precisely like the trunk of the 'satiable Elephant's Child.

---

precisely—*exactly*

Character Theme—Curiosity

Thinking It Through

1. Why did the Elephant's Child get popped so much?

2. What did the Crocodile do to the Elephant's Child's nose?

3. What were some of the things the Elephant's Child used his trunk for?

4. Is this a true story? How do you know?

5. Who do you think "Best Beloved" is in this story?

THE ELEPHANT

When people call this beast to mind,
  They marvel more and more
At such a *little* tail behind,
  So LARGE a trunk before.

—*Hilaire Belloc*

The Hippopotamus

In the squdgy river,
  Down the oozely bank,
Where the ripples shiver,
  And the reeds are rank.

Where the purple Kippo
  Makes an awful fuss,
Lives the hip-hip-hippo
  Hippo-pot-a-mus!

---

rank—*in a row*

Broad his back and steady;
  Broad and flat his nose;
Sharp and keen and ready
  Little eyes are those.

You would think him dreaming
  Where the mud is deep.
It is only seeming—
  He is not asleep.

Better not disturb him,
  There'd be an awful fuss
If you touched the Hippo,
  Hippo-pot-a-mus.

—*Georgia Roberts Durston*

Habits of the Hippopotamus

The hippopotamus is strong
    And huge of head and broad of bustle;
The limbs on which he rolls along
    Are big with hippopotomuscle.

He does not greatly care for sweets
    Like ice cream, apple pie, or custard,
But takes to flavor what he eats
    A little hippopotomustard.

The hippopotamus is true
    To all his principles, and just;
He always tries his best to do
    The things one hippopotomust.

He never rides in trucks or trams,
    In taxicabs or omnibuses,
And so keeps out of traffic jams
    And other hippopotomusses.

—*Arthur Guiterman*

omnibus—*a bus*

Paul Bunyan, Northwoods Lumberman

an American tall tale   *Walter Blair*

Paul Bunyan worked
at lumbering a long time. He started lumbering
back there in Maine, where he was born, in the
early days of lumbering. Later he moved to Wisconsin, Minnesota, North Dakota—along in there,
and logged that part of the country.

Whenever there's any doubt about where a
great man was born, any number of places are
likely to fight for the honor. It was so with Paul,
as was to be expected. But there is some reason
for saying that he *may* have been born several
places all at once, since he was large enough,
even at the start, to need some scope for being
born in. Mostly, though, he was born in the state
of Maine.

---

scope—*room*

At three weeks, baby Paul got his family into a bit of trouble by kicking around his little tootsies and knocking down something like four miles of standing timber. This was in Maine, and remembering the old saying, "As goes Maine, so goes the nation," the government took action right away. They told Paul's family they'd have to move the little fellow somewhere or other where he'd do less damage.

With the timber Paul had kicked over, the family made Paul a cradle, which they anchored off Eastport. Everything went well until, getting playful, Paul began waving his arms and legs around, the way babies do. That started the cradle rocking, and that started a bunch of waves that larruped around and came close to drowning every town along the New England coast.

So they had to move him again—keep him some place ashore until he was a year or two old and could shift for himself and watch out about hurting people. By that time, Paul had invented fishing and hunting, modern style, and had started, so to speak, to invent logging.

People had done some logging, if you could call it that, on a small scale B.P.B. (Before Paul

---

tootsies—*a child's term for feet*   larrup—*to whip; beat*

Bunyan). But since Paul figured out all the best dodges in the business, you might say he invented it. Then he went out and perfected it in his own way, and trimmed it up with Efficiency and Mass Production, until nobody could come within ten miles of doing what Paul could.

When Paul came along, all lumbermen did in the way of logging was chop trees down any old way and then, in a haphazard fashion, get the logs to the sawmill. Sometimes it would be so much bother and take so long to do this, that it was scarcely worth the trouble.

But Paul changed all that in short order.

At the start, for instance, the way ax-men kept their axes sharpened was most awkward. The ax-man would go up to the top of a hill, find a big stone, and start it rolling. Then he'd gallop downhill alongside the stone, holding his ax against the stone.

"That won't do," says Paul, just like that. "If the stone's bumpy, or if the hill is, you get the ax sharp, maybe, but the blade's likely to have too many scallops in it, pretty much like a washboard. Guess I'll invent a grindstone."

---

haphazard—*not planned; casual*
scallops—*a series of curves along the edge of something*

washboard—*a board with a ridged surface*

Which he did. And that ended that kind of trouble, and saved the men the work of running so much.

Everything men did in logging had to be worked out by Paul. He had to figure out how to mark his logs so they wouldn't be swiped by other companies, how to get the logs down river, how to break up log jams—how to do most everything that had been done either very badly or not at all before Paul came along.

After he'd perfected processes and methods all along the line, things went smoothly everywhere they'd gone roughly before. And when he'd lined up his help, both animal and human, Paul Bunyan had a set-up that couldn't help but be world famous.

Babe, the Blue Ox, was the most useful of the

animals. They say he was sky-blue because of his being born in the Winter of the Blue Snow, though most of us historians think this explanation is a little silly. If this was so, we'd like to know, why'd he have a black nose and white horns? Anyhow, Babe was a big beast—forty-two ax-handles between the horns—and strong in proportion.

Some ways, Babe was a bother. Supplies for a monster animal like that were naturally a problem. Every time Babe needed to be shod, they'd have to open a new iron mine on Lake Superior. Then there was the problem of feeding him. In one day, he could eat all the feed one crew could lug to camp in a whole leap year. Another thing about the brute that was bothersome was his sense of humor. Nothing he could think up seemed cuter to Babe than sneaking up behind a drive and drinking up the river, until the logs were as dry as a skeleton and even less likely to move. And his other playful pranks were likely to be similarly gruesome.

But all in all, Babe doubtless was more useful than he was bothersome. Take the way he

---

shod—*provided with shoes*
drive—*a collection of logs being floated down a river to a sawmill*

had with crooked roads. That stretch in Wisconsin showed what he could do. It was nineteen miles long as the crow flies, but much longer if you had to follow it, because it jogged and jiggled around and doubled back on itself so often. The teamsters kept twisting around until they were dizzy. Then, on top of that, they kept meeting themselves on the way back, so that they began to get the jumping jim-jams. Result was, Paul decided to hitch Babe to the end of this road and straighten her out.

Babe scowled, put his tongue in one corner of his mouth, hunched his shoulders, and just

teamster—*a person who hauls loads by truck or by teams of animals*

about touched the ground with his belly. His legs were quivering like daddy-longleg legs before he could get started moving. Finally, though, after he'd started going, he kept going until he'd pulled her straight. And there was enough road left over—fifty-three miles and a fraction—to do a number of useful things with; I don't recall exactly what.

Things like that, helpful little things, seemed to more than make up for all the trouble Babe brought to Paul's men. Besides, Paul was most fond of the animal, and Babe had a great liking for Paul. Babe would do anything in his power for Paul, unless it was impossible.

Character Theme—Resourcefulness

Thinking It Through

1. Where was Paul Bunyan born, "mostly"?
2. Why did the government tell his parents they would have to move him?
3. What were some bothersome things about Babe's size?
4. Give an example of Babe's humor.
5. What very helpful thing did Babe do?
6. What was the first clue that this story could not have happened?

Mary Indoors

Aren't you coming out, Mary?
   Come out: your eyes will tire—
Oh, let me be, please, please, said she,
   I want to read by the fire.

What are you reading, Mary,
   That keeps you, keeps you in?—
Oh, wonderful things of knights and kings,
   With their heart's desire to win.

Look out of window, Mary!
   The blustering day is bright.
Come fight the wind with us, and find
   The sun on the hilly height.

Come on out of it, Mary,
   And win your heart's desire!—
Oh, let me be, please, *please*, said she,
   I want to read by the fire.

—*Eleanor Farjeon*

---

desire—*to want or long for*
blustering—*windy*

The Legend of William Tell

Amy Cruse

In 1307, the Emperor of Austria determined to bring Switzerland under his power. He laid heavy taxes upon the country and placed his own officers over the people. One of the cruelest and most oppressive of these officers was Gessler, who ruled the Canton of Uri.

The ill treatment which they received from their Austrian rulers finally forced the Swiss to rebel. The Swiss leaders met in secret and vowed to fight to the death to free their country from the tyrant. One of these leaders was William Tell, a hardy mountaineer and a famous archer. He lived in the canton over which the cruel Gessler ruled.

---

oppressive—*cruel; unjust*
canton—*a small division of Switzerland*

tyrant—*a harsh ruler*
archer—*one who shoots with a bow and arrow*

William Tell went one day, taking with him his seven-year-old son, to the little town of Altdorf, which was near his home. The two went happily along together until they came to the marketplace; but to the little boy's disappointment, scarcely a person was to be seen. There was no pleasant stir and bustle, such as had delighted him on former visits, and he looked round curiously to see if he could discover the cause.

All was as usual except that in the middle of the marketplace a great pole was stuck up, and on the top of the pole was a hat—a very grand hat with a feather and a gold buckle. Four Austrian soldiers stood on each side of the pole.

William Tell, holding his little son by the hand, walked straight across the square, taking no notice of the hat or of the soldiers who guarded it. But he had gone only a few steps past them when they rushed out upon him.

"Throw him into prison!" they cried. "He has not bowed to Gessler's hat, which stands there as a sign of the might of Austria. Gessler has commanded that all who pass by shall do it reverence, and this man has not even glanced toward it."

They seized William Tell roughly, while the frightened child clung closely to him. With

seize—*to grab suddenly; to take by force*

flashing eyes Tell pushed them away and stood looking so fiercely on them that for a moment they hung back. People came running into the marketplace from the houses and streets round about, and a great commotion arose. Tell was well known in the town, and many voices were raised to explain to him what was going on.

The hated Gessler had placed the hat in the square that morning. Some few of the inhabitants of Altdorf had bowed before it, but most had kept out of the marketplace.

While the men of Altdorf were pouring out this story to William Tell, Gessler himself rode into the marketplace. He saw who it was that his soldiers had taken prisoner, and a smile of satisfaction came upon his cruel face. He knew Tell well and hated him for his strength and courage and skill which helped to make him a leader among his fellows.

When Tell saw the governor, he cried out boldly, "I appeal for justice. Bid these men let me go. I have done no wrong."

Gessler got down from his horse and came toward the excited group. The people drew back from him with dark and sullen looks and angry

---

commotion—*a disturbance*   sullen—*resentful*
appeal—*to make an earnest*
 or urgent request

murmurs. He looked round on them with the cruel smile still on his face.

"You shall have justice," he said, "more than justice. You shall have a chance to win your pardon for this disobedience. Men say that you have wonderful skill as an archer." He turned to his soldiers. "Take an apple," he commanded, "and put it on this child's head. Then let him stand under that linden tree, and let the father shoot at the apple. If he hits it, he shall go free."

Tell caught the hand of his son, who through all the disturbance had clung closely to him, then turned and looked at Gessler. He did not speak, but the people round about—there was a great crowd now—made a loud, angry murmuring.

But the little boy laughed happily. This, he thought, was an easy thing to do. He had seen his father hit smaller marks than an apple, at a distance greater than this to the linden tree, which could not be more than a hundred and fifty paces. It would be all right, and they would soon be free; and the people, Gessler, and his Austrians, and all, would see how well his father could shoot.

---

linden tree—*a type of shade tree*

He pulled his hand from his father's and took the apple the soldier had brought. Then he ran over to the linden tree, laughing joyously.

"Shoot now, Father," he cried, placing the apple on his head. "I will stand quite still."

Very slowly Tell took his bow. The people were very quiet, except the Austrian soldiers, who were laughing rudely.

"He will not do it," said Gessler with a sneer; "these Swiss dogs are cowards and no marksmen, though they boast so loudly of what they can do."

Tell took two arrows from his quiver, put one inside the bosom of his tunic, and with the other

---

quiver—*a case for holding arrows*
tunic—*a loose outer coat*

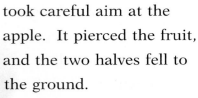

took careful aim at the apple. It pierced the fruit, and the two halves fell to the ground.

The little boy, with pride and delight, picked up the pieces and ran with them toward the group of Swiss and Austrians.

"See what my father has done!" he shouted. "Here is the apple."

Then the others found their voices. The Swiss cried out in triumph; the Austrians muttered angrily. Gessler's face was very dark.

William Tell stood silent in the midst, showing neither joy nor triumph. He lifted the little boy and kissed him. As he set him down, Gessler spoke.

"Why did you take two arrows when you were to shoot only one?" he asked.

Tell looked at him steadily. "I meant the second for you," he said, "if with the first I killed my son."

Character Theme—Courage, Love of Family,
& Trust

308

Thinking It Through

1. In what canton of Switzerland did William Tell live?

2. Whom did the Emperor of Austria place over this canton?

3. Why was William Tell seized?

4. What did Gessler do when Tell appealed for justice?

5. Which of these words would you use to describe William Tell's son—courageous, athletic, confident, talented? Why?

We
Understand
So Little
A Jewish folktale

Once there were two young brothers who
had spent all their lives in the city, and had never
seen a field or pasture. So one day they decided
to take a trip into the countryside. As they were
walking along, they spied a farmer plowing, and
were puzzled about what he was doing.

"What kind of behavior is this?" they asked
themselves. "This fellow marches back and forth
all day, scarring the earth with long ditches. Why
should anyone destroy such a pretty meadow like
that?"

Later in the afternoon they passed the same
place again, and this time they saw the farmer
sowing grains of wheat in the furrows.

"Now what's he doing?" they asked themselves. "He must be a madman. He's taking
perfectly good wheat and tossing it into these
ditches!"

---

sowing—*planting*

furrows—*long, narrow grooves
made in the ground by a plow*

"The country is no place for me," said one of the brothers. "The people here act as if they had no sense. I'm going home." And he went back to the city.

But the second brother stayed in the country, and a few weeks later he saw a wonderful change. Fresh green shoots began to cover the field with a lushness he had never imagined. He quickly wrote to his brother and told him to hurry back to see the miraculous growth.

So his brother returned from the city, and he too was amazed at the change. As the days passed, they saw the green earth turn into a golden field of tall wheat. And now they understood the reason for the farmer's work.

Then the wheat grew ripe, and the farmer came with his scythe and began to cut it down. The brother who had returned from the city couldn't believe it. "What is this foolish man doing now?" he exclaimed. "All summer long he worked so hard to grow this beautiful wheat, and now he's destroying it with his own hands! He is a madman after all! I've had enough. I'm going back to the city."

But his brother had more patience. He stayed in the country and watched the farmer

---

lushness—*rich growth of plants*

scythe (sīth)—*a long-handled tool used for cutting grain*

collect the wheat and take it to his granary. He
saw how cleverly he separated the chaff, and how
carefully he stored the rest. And he was filled
with awe when he realized that by sowing a bag
of seed, the farmer had harvested a whole field of
grain. Only then did he truly understand that the
farmer had a reason for everything he did.

"And this is how it is with God's works, too,"
he said. "We mortals see only the beginnings of

chaff—*the useless husks of
wheat or other grains*

mortals—*humans*

His plan. We cannot understand the full purpose and end of His creation. So we must have faith in His wisdom."

Character Theme—Wisdom

Thinking It Through

1. What was the farmer's first step in growing wheat?

2. When the first brother saw the farmer cutting his wheat, what did he think the farmer had done?

3. When did the second brother finally realize that the farmer knew what he was doing?

4. What did the brothers learn by watching the farmer?

From the Bible

For My thoughts are not your thoughts, neither are your ways My ways, saith the Lord. For as the heavens are higher than the earth, so are My ways higher than your ways, and My thoughts than your thoughts.
—Isaiah 55:8–9

KNOWLEDGE

Your mind is a meadow
To plant for your needs;
You are the farmer,
With knowledge for seeds.

Don't leave your meadow
Unplanted and bare,
Sow it with knowledge
And tend it with care.

Who'd be a know-nothing
When he might grow
The seed of the knowledge
Of stars and of snow;

The science of numbers,
The stories of time.
The magic of music,
The secrets of rhyme?

Don't be a know-nothing!
Plant in the spring,
And see what a harvest
The summer will bring.

—*Eleanor Farjeon*

THE BOOK LOST AT SEA

Hugh T. Kerr (adapted)

Years ago, somebody on a ship dropped a
book overboard, and it fell into the sea. It must
have belonged to some tourist or visitor who had
been reading it on deck when the wind suddenly
lifted it out of his hands, and it was carried out on

the deep sea and fell face down upon the waves. There it floated like a little boat. How long it floated nobody knows, but it ended up in a bay off the coast of Japan. The seagulls pecked at it and thought it was bread, and the fish played around it, and nobody might ever have heard of it had not God meant to use it. And so it was found.

It was found by a Japanese soldier named Mr. Murata who was commander of the army at Nagasaki.

One day he noticed something floating on the waves and set about to get it. He was interested in it immediately, for it was a strange thing to find floating on the sea. He turned its wet pages, but he could not read it, because it was printed in English. It was not printed like any other book he had ever seen. It seemed to be broken up into chapters and little verses, each of which was numbered.

He was a cultured gentleman, and he decided to find out what this strange book he so strangely found was. He discovered that it was the Christians' Bible.

The Japanese hated the Christians at this

Murata (mo͞o·rä′tə)
Nagasaki (nä·gə′sä′ke̅)
cultured—*well educated; refined in manners, interests, etc.*

time. Indeed, there was a fearful old law which read:

> So long as the sun shall warm
> the earth, let no Christian be so bold
> as to come to Japan; and let us know
> that the king of Spain himself or the
> Christian's God, or the great God of all,
> if he violate this command, shall pay
> for it with his head.

This only made the strange book more interesting to Mr. Murata and, being a soldier, he knew no fear. Since he knew how to read the Chinese language, he sent to China and got a Chinese copy of the Book he had found. He read it through. He was interested, and he read it through again. He read it again, and then he longed to have someone tell him about it.

An American missionary named Dr. Verbeck came to Japan five years after Mr. Murata found the Bible floating on the sea. The missionary came to live in the very city where Murata was! For seven years now, he had been trying to share the gospel, but everyone was afraid to listen to him.

So it was that, twelve years after finding the floating Bible, Mr. Murata's search came to an end. With his brother, his two sons, and a number of his friends, he went to see the missionary.

"Sir," said Mr. Murata, after telling Dr. Verbeck about the floating Bible, "I cannot tell you

my feelings when, for the first time, I read the
account of the character and work of Jesus Christ.
I had never seen, nor heard, nor imagined such
a Person. I was filled with admiration, over-
whelmed with emotion, and taken captive by the
record of His nature and life."

The men talked for hours with the missionary.
At last, knowing it could cost them their lives, Mr.
Murata and some of those with him believed in
Jesus and were baptized.

Before long the laws were changed, and in
time there were hundreds of churches and thousands of Christians in the beautiful land of Japan,
and it all began with a Bible that had fallen into
the sea.

It is wonderful how great things grow out
of little things. The mighty oak
comes from the little
acorn, and the golden
harvest from a few
sacks of grain,
and some-
times a life is
changed by a

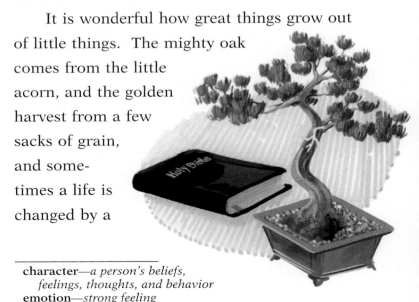

character—*a person's beliefs,
feelings, thoughts, and behavior*
emotion—*strong feeling*

little touch of kindness, a little word of love, or a person who is willing to let God work in his heart.

Character Theme—Courage & Faith

Thinking It Through

1. Who found the book floating in the sea? What was his profession?
2. How many years passed after Mr. Murata found the Bible before the missionary explained it to him?
3. How did Mr. Murata and some of those with him show their courage when they went to see the missionary?
4. What were some of the results of Mr. Murata's finding the Bible?

From the Bible

For the Word of God is quick, and powerful, and sharper than any twoedged sword, piercing even to the dividing asunder of soul and spirit, and of the joints and marrow, and is a discerner of the thoughts and intents of the heart. *—Hebrews 4:12*

Thy Word

Thy Word is like a garden, Lord,
    With flowers bright and fair;
And every one who seeks may pluck
    A lovely cluster there.
Thy Word is like a deep, deep mine;
    And jewels rich and rare
Are hidden in the mighty depths
    For every searcher there.

Thy Word is like a starry host;
    A thousand rays of light
Are seen to guide the traveler,
    And make his pathway bright.
Thy Word is like an armory,
    Where soldiers may repair,
And find for life's long battle-day
    All needful weapons there.

Oh, may I love Thy precious Word;
    May I explore the mine;
May I its fragrant flowers glean;
    May light upon me shine.
Oh, may I find my armor there;
    Thy Word my trusty sword,
I'll learn to fight with every foe
    The battle of the Lord.

—Author Unknown

---

armory—*a storehouse for weapons*
repair—*to go*
foe—*enemy*

Moni and His Goats

A story from Switzerland
Johanna Spyri

It was very early in the morning when Moni,
the goat boy, came through the little Swiss village
singing his song. The goats sprang from their
sheds to meet him as he waved his switch and
called to them.

In the sky, the rosy clouds were piled high,
and a fresh morning breeze whispered about the
ears of Moni as he climbed upward. How pleasant it all was! Everything was the way he liked to
have it. The boy sang out of pure happiness.

Moni and the goats climbed upward for
about two hours until they were high among
the peaks of the mountains. The higher they
climbed, the brighter everything seemed. Once
more the goat boy began to sing from the bottom
of his heart, louder and more joyously the farther
up he went. And this is the song that rang out
among the mountain peaks:

Moni (mä′nē)

321

Sing, birds, on the high slopes;
Sing where the fir trees grow.
Whenever you sing, the sun comes out,
And the rain is sure to go.

Moni kept on climbing until he reached a little green mountain meadow. In this spot he often stayed for hours at a time while his animals grazed quietly about him. He took his little sack of bread and cheese from his back and laid it in a small hollow of the ground which he had long ago dug out. Then he threw himself down on the fragrant grass among the yellow and purple flowers and looked happily about him.

The sky was now a deep blue. On all sides of Moni were the high mountains with their snow-covered peaks that seemed to reach to the very sky itself. Moni lay whistling joyously, while a pleasant mountain breeze cooled his warm face. If he stopped whistling for a moment, the birds took up the song as they flew off into the blue sky. The goat boy was perfectly happy.

From time to time Meggie, the youngest kid, would come up and rub her little head on Moni's shoulder. Then she would give a loving bleat and go around to the other side of the boy and rub against him once more. The rest of the

---

fragrant—*smelling good*

flock came, one after the other, to see the goat-
herd, and each of the animals had his own way of
showing his love for Moni.

When Brownie, Moni's own goat, came for
his visit, he walked around the boy very carefully
as if he were making sure that everything was
just as usual. And he would not go away until
Moni said, "Yes, yes, Brownie, everything is all
right. Now go back to your grazing."

So the sunny morning passed. Finally Moni
sat up and leaned thoughtfully on the staff that
he always carried to help him over the rough
places. He was wondering if he might try to
climb a new side of the mountain this afternoon.
It would be fun to lead the goats high up to the
Three Dragon Stones, where the tenderest grass
and bushes grew. The way was steep, and there
were dangerous places on the mountain wall; but
he knew a good path, and the goats were always
very careful.

So, after eating his lunch, Moni started up to
the Three Dragon Stones, with the goats climbing
joyfully after him. Soon most of them had run
ahead of him except little Meggie, who always
stayed near at hand. At first everything went very
well. With long leaps the goats rushed forward to
the green bushes and grass on the slopes above.

Ahead of them all ran the light-footed Swallow, a small, white goat, springing from rock to rock. Today she was to have a surprise.

Halfway up, the young goat stopped suddenly. Before her stood a wild chamois looking curiously at her. Such a thing had never happened to Swallow before. She stood still, waiting for the stranger to move aside so that she could jump to the rock above. But the wild mountain antelope did not stir from Swallow's path; he kept on looking boldly into her eyes.

How long they would have been standing there I do not know, if Great Sultan, the oldest and largest goat, had not caught up to them just in time to see what was happening. He passed Swallow carefully and pushed the chamois to one side roughly. Swallow turned her soft eyes to the Great Sultan as if to thank him, and then bounded away.

And now it seemed as if the swift and daring Swallow had set a bad example for the other goats. Some of them began to leap so quickly from rock to rock that Moni had to cry out warningly: "Take it easy! Take it easy! Don't crowd in the steep places, or one of you will be down below in a moment with a broken leg."

---

light-footed—*stepping lightly and gracefully*
chamois (shăm′ē)
antelope—*a swift, cud-chewing, deerlike animal in the same family as cattle, sheep, and goats*

Scarcely had the goat boy paused for breath when he cried out again in fright, "Swallow, what has got into your head?" The swift goat had now climbed as high as the Dragon Stones and had bounded up to the very edge of one of them, where she stood looking saucily down at him. Moni moved like lightning in the next few moments. If Swallow should make a single step forward, she would fall many feet below! The boy climbed hurriedly up and drew her back.

"You come down with me, little silly," he scolded.

Moni led Swallow down and held her until she had forgotten all about her desire to run away.

"Where is Meggie?" shouted Moni suddenly as he saw Blackie, Meggie's mother, standing all by herself on the edge of a steep, rocky wall. The young kid was always near her mother if she was not beside Moni. "What have you done with your kid, Blackie?" Moni cried, hurrying to where the goat stood.

The mother goat behaved very strangely. She ate nothing and stood in one spot with her ears pointed as if listening. Moni reached her side and stood listening also. Suddenly he heard a faint bleat. It was Meggie's voice coming up from

---

saucily—*in a bold, spirited manner*

below, a pitiful and frightened call for help. Moni
lay down on the ground and leaned over the edge.
Far below there was something moving, and he
saw that it was Meggie hanging over the bough of
a tree that grew out from the cliff.

"Oh, she must have fallen down!" cried Moni.

Fortunately, the branch had caught the little goat, or she would have fallen many feet below. But even now, if she could not keep her place, she would fall and be dashed to pieces. In the most anxious tone, Moni called down, "Hold on, Meggie; hold fast to the branch. See, I am coming to get you."

But how could he save the kid that was bleating so piteously below? The mountain wall was so steep that he could not climb down it. Moni thought hard. The little goat must be about on a level with the Rain Cliff, an overhanging rock under which the goat boys gathered for shelter when a mountain storm arose. From that spot Moni thought he could climb upward to the tree on which Meggie was hanging.

Quickly the boy whistled his herd together and led them to a level spot near the Rain Cliff. There he left them to graze and went on by himself to the Cliff. When he looked up at poor Meggie, she seemed to be very high above him. Moni saw that it was going to be hard to reach the young goat, and still harder to climb down again with Meggie on his back. But that was the only way to save the little animal.

So the boy started at once to climb up the cliff until he reached the tree. Then he made

his way to the bough on which the frightened little animal hung. Grasping the trembling kid fast in both hands, he raised her to his shoulders, and with the greatest care climbed back down. When his feet touched firm earth again and he saw that Meggie was safe, he cried, "Oh, dear God, I thank Thee a thousand times for helping me to save Meggie. How happy we both are!"

Then Moni sat down and stroked the kid, whose delicate limbs still trembled with fright. And when it was time to lead the flock homeward, the goat boy took the kid in his arms, saying tenderly, "Come, poor Meggie, you are still shaking. You can't walk home. I will carry you."

And so he carried the little animal the whole way down, and the villagers who came to get their goats from Moni heard the story and were filled with surprise. They had always thought that the goat boy had nothing to do all day but lie in a cool mountain pasture, singing his songs.

Character Theme—Compassion & Contentment

Thinking It Through

1. In what country did Moni live?
2. What was Moni's job?
3. How can you tell that Moni enjoyed his work?
4. Why did Moni lead the goats up to the Three Dragon Stones?
5. How did Moni know that something was wrong with Meggie?

I Stood Alone

I stood alone at sunset
    And watched the clouds drift by;
Each was tinted, shaped and shaded
    By the Painter of the sky.
The heavens were a glory
    With their ever-changing scene,
And the symphony of the color
    Made the landscape calm, serene.

I stood alone at twilight
    Beside a shadowed lake
And listened to the music
    That the woodland creatures make,
The singing of the crickets,
    The whippoorwill's sweet call,
And I reveled in God's presence,
    He Who "marks the sparrow's fall."

I stood alone at nightfall
    As the last blush of the day
Had surrendered to the darkness
    On the hilltops far away—
And there on the horizon,
    Brilliant as a fabled gem,
Was the evening star, God's handwork,
    Shining forth its praise to Him.

—*G. Kearnie Keegan*

tinted—*given a delicate, pale color*
serene—*peaceful*
revel—*to take delight in*

330

The Persian and His Sons

An old tale retold by
William James Sly

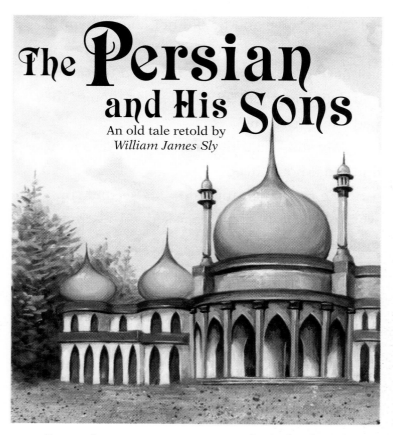

Once there was a Persian ruler who lived in a great palace with his three sons. The father had a beautiful pearl which he decided to give to the son who showed himself the noblest. He called the three boys before him and asked each to tell the noblest deed he had performed in the last month.

The eldest said, "Father, as I was traveling in a foreign land, a merchant trusted me with many

---

Persian—*of or from ancient Iran*
noble—*having or showing greatness*
  of character; worthy of praise

valuable jewels, and he did not count them. I might easily have kept one or two and they would not have been missed, but I carried those jewels and delivered them all as safely as though they had been my own."

"My son," said the father, "you were honest and did a noble deed!"

The ruler then turned to his second son. "And what of you, my son?" he asked. "Have you, too, done a noble deed?"

"Father," said the second son, "as I was walking in the country the other day, I saw a child playing by a lake. While I watched, the child fell in, and I saved him."

"You have done your duty," said the father, "and you, too, have done a noble deed."

Only the third son was left. Turning to him, the ruler asked, "And what have you to say, my son?"

"Father," said the third boy, "as I crossed over the mountain the other day, I saw a man who had done me a great wrong. He was sleeping near the edge of a dangerous precipice. I would have walked by without a word, only something within me called me to go back and awake him lest he fall over the precipice and be killed. I did this,

---

precipice—*a steep cliff*

knowing all the time that the man would not understand, and that he would be angry with me, as, indeed, he was."

"My son," cried the father, "your deed was the noblest. To do good to an enemy without hope of reward is indeed the noblest of all. The pearl is yours!"

Character Theme—Honesty & Kindness

Thinking It Through

1. The father called one of the sons honest. What did that son do?

2. The father said that one of the sons did his duty. What did that son do?

3. Do you think the third son deserved the pearl? Why?

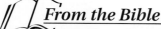

From the Bible

Ye have heard that it hath been said, Thou shalt love thy neighbor, and hate thine enemy.

But I say unto you, Love your enemies, bless them that curse you, do good to them that hate you, and pray for them which despitefully use you, and persecute you.

—Matthew 5:43–44

TRUE NOBILITY

Who does his task from day to day
And meets whatever comes his way,
Believing God has willed it so,
Has found real greatness here below.

Who guards his post, no matter where,
Believing God must need him there,
Although but lowly toil it be,
Has risen to nobility.

For great and low there's but one test:
'Tis that each man shall do his best.
Who works with all the strength he can
Shall never die in debt to man.

—*Edgar Guest*

---

lowly—*humble, ordinary*
in debt—*owing something*

Robinson Crusoe's New Home

adapted from *Robinson Crusoe*
Daniel DeFoe

Robinson Crusoe is an exciting book that you will want to read when you are older. It tells the adventures of a man who learned how to survive when he was left alone on a desert island. This part tells how he got to the island and something of his life there.

When I was a little boy, I lived in a great city by the sea. My father and mother were very kind to me and loved me dearly. They wanted me to go to school and learn many things so that I could some day be a useful man, but I was lazy. I thought it was much more fun to play by the river than to study. I often sat for hours watching the great ships loading and unloading their cargoes. As they sailed away, I wished that I could go with them to strange lands far away.

cargo—*goods carried by a ship, train, truck, or airplane*

Father said to me one day when I was older, "Robinson, I want you to be a merchant, like me. If you work hard at it, you shall someday take charge of my business. But if you are lazy, no one will have any use for you, and you will not be able to take care of yourself." He talked to me a long time about my bad habits.

"But, Father, I do not want to be a merchant," I said. "I want to go away on one of those ships. I want to visit new lands."

My father replied, "My son, if you do not learn anything, you will be of no use to anyone on the ship, and one must work in other countries as well as here. You must remember that idleness is the beginning of all mischief. If you disobey your father and mother and run away, you will be sorry one day, for whoever disobeys his parents will never be happy."

While he was talking, the tears ran down his face, and I could not help but feel that I ought to do as he wished. But very soon, when my father was not near, I threw my work aside, put on my hat, and went to the harbor. As I sat watching the ships, I wanted more than ever to sail away.

As I was walking along the harbor one day, I

---

merchant—*one who buys and sells goods*

met a friend, the son of the captain of one of the vessels.

After talking awhile, my friend said, "Well, Robinson, Father starts on a voyage today, and I am going with him."

"Oh! How I wish I could go with you!" said I.

"Come along!" he said.

"But I don't have any money," I replied.

"Father will take you for nothing, I am sure," said my friend. "You can work for him."

"Good!" I said. "If he will let me work my way, I'll go with you."

The ship on which I found myself that bright September morning was a large one. I heard the cry, "All ha—a—nds! Up anchor, a—ho—oy!" At once everyone seemed to be filled with life. Orders were given rapidly. There was such a hurrying about and so many strange noises that I hardly knew what to make of it. Above all sounded the boom of a cannon; then the vessel moved slowly out of the harbor. In a short time, we were under-way.

I turned to look at the home I was leaving. At first, I could see the streets with the people passing up and down. Soon I could see only the church towers. Finally, they, too, faded from sight, and I was out on the great ocean.

Behind me and before me, to my right and to my left, I could see nothing but water. Then I began to think of what I had done. I remembered my father's tears and my mother's kindness, and here I was out on the ocean sailing away from parents, home, and friends.

After we had been sailing for many weeks, a strong wind arose, and the ship rocked so fearfully from side to side that I became dizzy. The storm grew worse, and I thought that every wave would surely swallow up the ship. Then suddenly the sky grew darker and the sailors started calling and shouting to each other. I thought every minute that the ship would sink, and I made up my mind that if I ever reached land I would go back home and stay there.

The wind and waves carried the ship before them, tossing it about like a nutshell. All on board thought that we were lost. Suddenly one of the sailors cried out, "Land!"

We all rushed out of the cabin to see where we were, but the waves broke over the deck with such fury that we were driven back into the cabin. Then, all at once, we felt a fearful shock. The vessel had struck a rock!

The sailors cried out, "The ship has sprung a leak!" Water started pouring into it. Everyone called for help, and each thought only of saving his own life. I told God that if He would spare my life, I would return home to my good parents as soon as possible.

A small boat was let down into the water, and all of the men jumped into it. We rowed a little way from the sinking vessel. Then a great wave that looked like a mountain came rolling toward our boat. The boat was overturned, and all of the men went down.

I was a good swimmer, but the waves were so strong that I could do nothing. Soon the waves

hurled me against a rock on the shore, and I clung to this with all my strength. Then I ran up the cliff and looked about for the sailors, but I did not see them. They had all been drowned! I was the only one whose life had been saved. When I saw this, I knelt down and thanked God for His mercy to me.

I was soaking wet and had no change of clothes. I was hungry and thirsty and did not know where to look for food or drink. I was also afraid that wild animals might attack me, and I had no gun.

It was getting dark, and I knew that I must look for a place to sleep. For a long time I stood still, not knowing what to do. At last I said, "I will do as the birds do, and rest in a tree." I soon found one with thick branches.

As I had nothing with which to defend myself but a knife, I cut a good stick. Then I climbed the tree, arranged myself carefully, and fell asleep. Being very tired, I slept soundly till morning.

When I awoke, the sun was shining brightly, and the sea was calm. I was weak from hunger and thirst. "What can I find for breakfast?" I asked myself. I got down from my bed and walked around looking for food, but I saw nothing but grass.

Not far away was a high hill, and I went up to have a look around. It took me half an hour to climb it, but when I had reached the top I could see a long distance away. I saw that there was water all around me, and this distressed me greatly.

"So I am on an island," I cried, "alone and without food or shelter. Oh, what will become of me!"

But when the need is greatest, then God's help is nearest. As I spoke, my eyes fell upon the ship. It lay about a mile from the shore and had not been broken to pieces by the storm, as I had supposed.

It was still resting on the rock. "I must reach that ship," I thought. "How can I do it?"

The water was so shallow that I could wade to within a quarter of a mile of the ship, and I swam the rest of the way. With the help of a rope, I climbed up to the deck. No sooner had I reached it than I was greeted by joyful barking. The ship's dog, Barry, jumped and sprang around me, rejoicing to see a friend once more. I, too, was glad to have a living being with me again.

I found many things on the ship that had not been injured at all. First of all I hunted for food. I found a chest of ship biscuits and gave some to Barry, who was nearly starved, and then ate all I wanted myself.

I gathered the things together that I wanted to take with me and built a raft by fastening a number of logs together by ropes and nailing some

boards upon these. Upon the raft I put the chest
of biscuits, a Bible, a flint for making a fire, a tool
chest, clothing, and many other things. I took also
two cats that I found roaming the decks of the
ship. I had found a bag of money, but this was
worthless to me, and so I left it behind.

With a broken oar I then rowed toward land.
Suddenly I heard a splashing behind me, and
turned about, much frightened. But it was only
Barry, the faithful dog, who was swimming after me.
I pulled him out of the water and onto the raft.

In a half hour I landed everything safely. My next care was to get my goods under cover. For this purpose I went to work to build myself a tent. I cut a few poles, set them into the ground in the form of a circle, the tops touching, and fastened the sail from the ship over them. Into this tent I put everything I had brought from the ship.

A few days later, I went out to the ship again. As I was rowing to land, a strong wind arose, and I had to hurry to reach the shore with my raft. I had barely reached it when the wind became so strong that the waves covered the ship. When the sea became quiet again, nothing could be seen of it. I felt very thankful that God had enabled me to get so much; for I thought, "How could I have lived without these things!"

In the days and months that followed, I planted seeds, built a shelter, and learned to hunt and fish. As my father had predicted, my life was very difficult. For many years I led a lonely life on the island. I had my Bible from the ship to read, however, and with God's help and much hard work I was able to get the things I needed for survival.

The only living creatures that came near me for many a day were the dog and two cats. I was very glad when I caught a parrot and taught it to call my name. It was a strange family which sat at table. Poll perched on my shoulder and ate from my hand. At my right side was always trusty Barry, the dog. The cats sat one on each side of the table.

One day, as I walked along the shore, I was much frightened to find a footprint on the sand. After this I kept watch, knowing that wild men from other islands sometimes came ashore.

Months passed, and as I was walking near the shore one day, I saw a boat come in. There were in it twenty or thirty men with some prisoners. One of the prisoners ran away to make his escape. He ran toward the place where I was hiding, and I saved him from his enemies.

At first the poor fellow was afraid of me. He had never seen a white man nor a gun. He was very grateful to me for having saved his life, and he proved a faithful, loving friend.

I soon became very fond of my new friend, whom I called Friday. I taught him about God and read to him from my Bible. When at last a ship came to the island and I went home, I took my friend Friday with me.

Character Theme—Industry, Obedience, & Resourcefulness

Thinking It Through

1. What was Robinson Crusoe like as a boy?

2. What wise advice did his father give him?

3. Where did Robinson Crusoe get most of the things he needed for survival on the island?

4. What animals did Robinson Crusoe take from the ship?

5. How do you think he was different when he finally got home?

The Greatest River in the World

Catherine O. Peare

You may have heard of Mark Twain, the famous author of *Tom Sawyer* and *Huckleberry Finn*. Did you know that "Mark Twain" was not his real name? He was really named Samuel Clemens, and he grew up along the Mississippi River in Missouri, just as Tom and Huck did. When Sam Clemens was 11, his father died, and he had to stop school and go to work. He worked as a typesetter and then as a printer. In the spring of 1857, he traveled down the Mississippi on a steamboat and decided to be a riverboat pilot. Here is the story of that trip and of how he found his pen name, "Mark Twain."

One day Sam Clemens happened to dip into a book about South America, and his eyes grew wider as he learned about the Amazon River in Brazil. Another great river, one that was four thousand miles long!

"I am going to South America to explore the Amazon!" he announced.

All he had to do was find a ship in New Orleans or New York that was going to South America. New Orleans seemed like a better idea than New York, so he boarded a steamer, the *Paul Jones,* and started south.

Sam Clemens hadn't forgotten his dream of being a steamboatman. He stood at the rail a while, watching the river grow wider and deeper. Then he left the rail and wandered all the way up to the pilothouse, which was flanked by two giant smokestacks. He stood at the door of the circular room, looking at the big wheel and the man whose hand rested on it.

"How would you like a young man to learn the river?" he asked politely.

"I wouldn't like it," the pilot growled at him. "Cub pilots are more trouble than they're worth."

Sam stood his ground. He had just decided that he was tired of being a printer. He wanted to be a river pilot.

"Do you know the Bowen boys?" he asked.

It turned out that the man did know the Bowen boys. In fact, he had taught Will Bowen to be a pilot. After that the pilot grew more friendly. For the next two weeks, while the *Paul Jones* journeyed down the river to New Orleans, Sam hung around the pilothouse and talked with the pilot.

The man standing at the big wheel had been on the Mississippi for many years. He had experienced great adventures. He had narrowly escaped

---

flanked—*having something at either side*
cub—*a beginner at a trade*

death at the hands of bad men who traveled the Mississippi. His steamship had almost exploded more than once. Or so he said, and so Sam believed. Sam hadn't yet learned that rivermen were full of tall yarns.

Sam hated to say good-bye at New Orleans. But he was headed for the Amazon in South America, or so he thought. He was due for a disappointment. There weren't any ships going to the Amazon. There weren't going to be any for at least ten years. Sam rushed back to his pilot friend.

"Please take me on as a cub pilot," he begged. "No!"

Sam didn't give up. He went back every day for three days. At last the pilot agreed to teach Sam Clemens to be a river pilot.

"It will cost you five hundred dollars," he said. Sam had only ten dollars.

"River pilots earn good pay," said Sam hopefully. "As soon as I'm a river pilot I'll pay you back."

It was agreed, and Sam Clemens started on one of the greatest adventures he was ever to have—his life on the Mississippi.

---

tall yarn—*a story that seems exaggerated or hard to believe*

The boat backed out from New Orleans at
four in the afternoon, and it was 'our watch'
until eight. Mr. Bixby, my chief, 'straightened
her up,' plowed her along past the sterns of
the other boats that lay at the levee, and then
said, "Here, take her; shave those steamships
as close as you'd peel as apple."

Sam, the Cub Pilot

For the first time in his life, Sam took hold
of the wheel and felt the steamboat move to his
command. The wheel was made of hard, heavy

watch—*a person's time to be*
on duty or on guard
stern—*the rear part of the ship*

levee—*the thick walls or*
dikes built up along a river
to prevent flooding

wood with sixteen spokes. It would have been taller than a man if it hadn't turned partly below the level of the floor. It was fully nine feet across. When the current was swift, the pilot had to place his foot, as well as his hands, on one of the spokes in order to keep the wheel steady.

Of course, Sam was afraid of going too close to the other boats, and he left far too much space. The pilot scolded him with a long torrent of words, and Sam's training had begun.

The Mississippi had to be memorized mile by mile. Every landmark along both shores meant something. Every town, every bend in the river, every island, every clump of trees—all the way from New Orleans to St. Louis.

"Memorize the shape of the Mississippi, too," he was told, "because when you're steering a boat in the pitch dark, you won't be able to see any landmarks."

Sam thought it would take him the rest of his life to memorize the shape of the Mississippi.

And that wasn't all. The river was always changing. A boat could come through a spot one time and find deep water. On the next trip it would find a dangerous sand bar. A pilot had to

---

spokes—*the handholds on a ship's steering wheel*
sandbar—*a ridge of sand formed in a river*

watch the changing color of the water to know the depth. He had to listen to the leadsmen shouting their measurements as they let down the line to find the bottom of the river.

"M-a-r-k three! M-a-r-k three! Quarter-less-three! Half twain! Quarter twain! M-a-r-k twain!"

These shouted measurements told the pilot that he was entering shallower water. The pilot pulled his bell ropes and gave correct bell signals to the men in the engine room for more speed or less. If the pilot made a mistake, he could wreck the boat, lose expensive cargo, perhaps even kill his passengers and crew.

---

leadsman (lĕdz′mən)—*a man who uses a line with a lead weight to measure the depth of the water*

mark twain—*two fathoms, or twelve feet, deep*

Sam decided that there was nobody in the world so important as a river pilot.

There were rainy, misty days on the river when everything seemed to change shape. And there were foggy nights when the pilot could see nothing at all. He still had to steer his boat.

Every once in a while Sam's teacher would test him with a question. "How much water did we have in the middle crossing at Hole-in-the-Wall, trip before last?"

Sam couldn't remember. Then would come a terrible scolding. "My boy, you've got to remember. You've got to remember the exact spot and the exact mark the boat lay in, in every one of the five hundred shoal places between St. Louis and New Orleans."

Sam wouldn't dare to answer.

"When I say I'll learn a man the river, I mean it," said the pilot gruffly. "You can depend on it, I'll learn him or kill him."

Sam Wins His License

Sam did learn the Mississippi, all the river's curves and bends, all the changes of the seasons, too. In the spring the water was much deeper than at the end of the summer. The melting

---

shoal—*a shallow place or a sandbar*

snows farther north did that. He learned the river going north, and he learned the river going south.

Sam Clemens learned the river so well that he became an expert. He studied with more than one pilot. He worked on a freight boat and then on a passenger boat, the *Pennsylvania*. Sam was getting closer and closer to his pilot's license.

He received his pilot's license in the fall when he was only twenty-three years old. It had taken him a year and a half of hard work and study. At last he was a riverboatman. He could vie with the best of them, and he could tell yarns as tall as any of them! Sometimes Sam Clemens' yarns were a little taller. He still read in his spare time and even wrote down some of the rivers tales that he heard.

He used to like to tell the yarn about the time he rescued on old man from a burning building. The man was hanging out of a window four flights up, calling for help. "The ladders weren't long enough. Nobody had enough presence of mind— nobody but me. I came to the rescue. I yelled for a rope. When it came I threw the old man the end of it. He caught it and I told him to tie it around his waist. He did so, and I pulled him down."

---

freight boat—*a boat that carries cargo or goods*
vie—*to compete*

Every once in a while a yarn that certainly sounded as though Sam Clemens had made it up was published in a local newspaper. He signed his short stories and humorous articles "Mark Twain," the river term which means "safe water."

Sam Clemens was a pilot on the Mississippi River for three years. He had just about forgotten that he wanted to go to South America and explore the Amazon River. The Amazon? Who cared a fig about the Amazon? The Mississippi was the greatest river in the world!

Character Theme—Perseverance

Thinking It Through

1. What was the name of the steamship Sam Clemens took down the Mississippi River?

2. Why did Sam go to New Orleans?

3. How much did Sam agree to pay to learn to be a river pilot?

4. Where did the name Mark Twain come from?

5. Why do you think Sam's teacher was so hard on him?

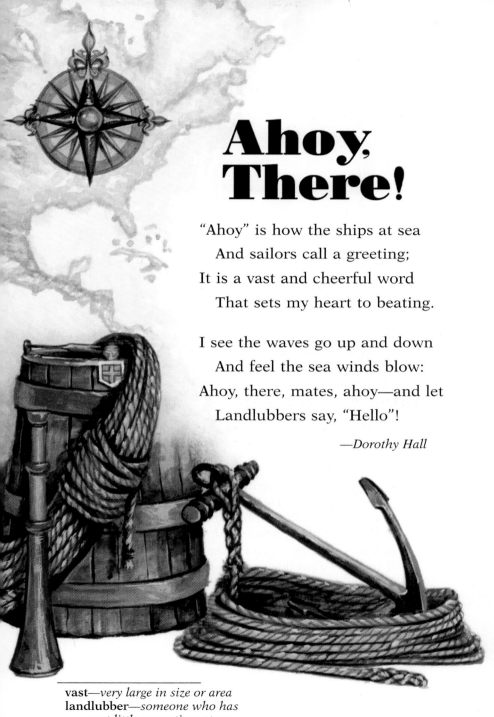

Ahoy, There!

"Ahoy" is how the ships at sea
    And sailors call a greeting;
It is a vast and cheerful word
    That sets my heart to beating.

I see the waves go up and down
    And feel the sea winds blow:
Ahoy, there, mates, ahoy—and let
    Landlubbers say, "Hello"!

—*Dorothy Hall*

vast—*very large in size or area*
landlubber—*someone who has
spent little or no time at sea*

Battle
with Death

Dorothy Haas

Louis Pasteur, a Frenchman, was one of the world's greatest scientists. He lived from 1822 until 1895. If you had milk with your breakfast this morning, that milk was probably *pasteurized,* or treated with heat against germs by a process that Pasteur developed. If you have a pet dog or cat at home, it has probably been vaccinated so that it will not get *rabies,* a terrible disease for which Pasteur found a cure. This story tells about Pasteur's experiences with rabies.

Louis Pasteur (lo͞o'ē păs·tûr')
pasteurization—*the use of heat for destroying harmful bacteria in milk*
rabies—*a life-threatening disease given to people by the bite of an infected animal*

If the people of little Louis Pasteur's village in France had been asked to guess what he would become when he grew up, few would have said he would become one of the world's greatest scientists. "Little Louis . . ." they would have said thoughtfully. "Well, have you seen any of the pictures he draws? They are really very good. He will probably grow up to be an artist."

Some of the scientist's boyhood drawings still exist. Artists agree that Louis Pasteur, scientist, could have been—Louis Pasteur, artist!

"Run for your life!"

"Mad wolf!"

A small boy pushed open the heavy door of his home. He slipped inside, slamming it behind him.

His heart pounding, little Louis Pasteur—for that was the boy's name—turned. He brushed aside the lace curtain on the window next to the door. The scene outside was something out of a nightmare.

A maddened, snarling wolf, foaming at the mouth, charged down the street. Panic-stricken people scattered before it. Some found shelter. Others, not so lucky, were bitten. Little Louis closed his eyes. He pressed his face into the

scratchy lace of the curtain. But he could not shut out those dreadful cries.

Soon the howls of the suffering beast faded in the distance. Then they stopped altogether. The wolf had gone back to the dark forests that surrounded Arbois. Silence returned to the tiny town.

Once more Louis dared to look outside. A pitiful parade was passing by. One by one, the wolf's victims were being helped up the street. They seemed to be going to the blacksmith's shop.

Louis pulled open the door and followed them. What he saw there was to haunt him for the rest of his life.

The only known treatment for rabies, caused by the bite of a mad animal, was a fearful one. Each of the wolf's victims—eight in all—was

---

Arbois (är·bwä′)

brought into the blacksmith's shop. There the doctor touched a red-hot poker to the wounds. He was trying to burn away the poisons left there by the sick wolf.

But the treatment was useless. In the weeks that followed, the wolf's victims sickened. At last, one by one, they died. There was no cure for rabies.

Many years passed. The little boy of Arbois grew up. He studied chemistry and biology. He became a scientist, an honored scientist known throughout France. In his laboratory he found the answers to many grave problems.

The farmers' sheep and cattle died in great numbers from a disease called anthrax. Dr. Louis Pasteur found a way to vaccinate them, and so to keep them healthy.

Many people became ill and died from drinking the milk of sick cows. Dr. Pasteur developed a method of making milk safe. We still use that method today. It is called pasteurization.

Many were the problems that the learned Dr. Pasteur solved. But during the years he could

poker—*an iron bar used for stirring a fire*
chemistry—*the study of matter*
biology—*the study of living things*
anthrax—*a dangerous disease of animals,
    especially cattle and sheep*

not forget the cries of the terrified townsfolk of Arbois.

The trouble was that no one knew quite where to start on the fearful problem of rabies, for nobody knew what caused the disease. Today we know that it is caused by a virus, a germ so small that it cannot be seen under the usual kind of microscope. But Dr. Pasteur did not know this.

One day, he was in his laboratory with his assistant. They were talking about rabies, as they often did. The elderly Dr. Pasteur, limping from an illness which had left him painfully crippled, moved up and down the long room as they talked.

"We do not know what causes rabies," he said. He paused for a thoughtful moment, leaning on his cane. "But every problem has an answer," he went on. "And to every answer there is a clue. Let's start looking for a clue. We will begin with the sick animals themselves!"

In the weeks that followed, strange guests came to live in Dr. Pasteur's Paris laboratory: mad rabbits, mad guinea pigs, mad dogs. The scientist studied the disease in these animals. He even studied the saliva which he took from their foaming mouths. But he did not find his clue.

---

virus—*an extremely tiny germ that causes disease*
saliva—*the watery fluid in the mouth that aids in swallowing and digesting food*

He tried making healthy animals sick in order to test ways of treating them. He injected into them the saliva of sick animals. Sometimes they got sick. Sometimes they did not, or unexpectedly got sick after long months of waiting. Dr. Pasteur was puzzled.

He worked long hours. He was in the laboratory, bent over his microscope, long before his assistant opened the door in the morning. And he stayed on, lost in thought, long after his assistant went home at night.

Months went by. Many times Dr. Pasteur thought he had the answer, only to meet with failure. But he did not give up. And then, at last, the long hours of work had their reward.

He injected nerve tissue from sick animals into healthy ones in a certain way. He found that in doing this he could, without fail, cause rabies in healthy animals. This was because the germs were concentrated in the nerve tissue. And this turned out to be the clue that Dr. Pasteur had been waiting for.

He found that by letting this tissue stand for a few days it became weak. When a dog received this weak nerve tissue it became sick, yes. But not so sick that it died. The dog got well. And after

---

concentrated—*most numerous in; collected in*

that, even if injected with the strongest nerve tissue, the dog did not develop rabies. Its body had built up strength against the disease. The dog was "immune."

The scientist knew that persons bitten by rabid dogs do not show signs of illness until nearly a month later. If resistance could be built up in these people before they showed signs of the disease, perhaps they might not sicken at all! He worked up a course of treatment. It would take fourteen days.

On the first day, a dose of very weak fourteen-day-old nerve tissue was to be given to a person who had been bitten. This was followed on the second day by a thirteen-day-old dose, and so on, until on the last day strong virus was to be given. During this time the person's body would be building up resistance. Finally, the victim would have so much resistance that he could not get sick.

Dr. Pasteur had found his cure for rabies— or he thought he had. It had been successful with dogs. Would it work as well on a human being? Perhaps it would harm, rather than help, a person who had been bitten!

---

immune—*protected from getting a certain disease*
rabid—*having rabies*
dose—*a specific amount of medicine to be taken*

At last he decided what he would do. He would try the treatment on himself! If he was not harmed by it, then he would be sure that it was safe for everyone.

But something happened before he had a chance to test his cure. It happened on July 6, 1885. Footsteps sounded on the stairway leading to the laboratory. The door was flung open. A woman rushed into the room.

"Dr. Pasteur!" she cried, when she spied the scientist. "I am Madame Meister. I have heard you are working on a cure for rabies. You must help my boy Joseph or he will surely die. We have come all the way from Alsace!" She turned and pointed to a young boy. He stood in the doorway, smiling shyly at the great scientist. Joseph Meister was nine years old. He had been bitten fourteen times.

Dr. Pasteur stood up, shaking his head. "But, my good woman!" he said. "The treatment has never been tried on a person. It may harm—"

Meister (mī′stẽr)

"Please, Doctor!" the woman pleaded. "You are our only hope!"

The scientist was thoughtful. "Let me think," he said. "I will let you know later today."

After Madame Meister and Joseph had gone, the scientist sat down at his desk. Should he use his treatment? Would he be risking great harm to a human life? Perhaps Joseph could live, in spite of his wounds. . . .

He talked to two of his doctor friends who knew of his work. They went with him to examine Joseph.

When they had finished, they turned to their friend. "The boy will surely die," they said. "But if you try your treatment, he at least stands a chance of living. By all means, try it!"

Treatment began that very day. In the days that followed, Dr. Pasteur and Joseph became good friends. The scientist watched his young friend worriedly. What if the treatment did not help. . . .

At last the day came when Joseph received the last and strongest dose of the nerve tissue. Dr. Pasteur waited. That night, the light in his laboratory burned on long after all the other houses on the street grew dark and silent.

Morning came. The sun rose. The city came alive with the sounds of horses and heavy wagons in the street below. Suddenly there was the sound of flying feet on the stairway. Once more the laboratory door burst open and Madame Meister stood there.

"Dr. Pasteur!" she cried. "Come!" She was gone.

Louis Pasteur limped hurriedly after her. At last he reached Joseph's room. He stopped, his hand on the doorknob. What would he find inside? Would his little friend be well, or would he. . . . He pushed open the door.

There, sitting up in the big bed, was a smiling boy. A pale—but healthy—Joseph! Beside him stood his mother, tears in her eyes and a smile on her lips.

Joseph gave a little bound, setting the old wooden bed to creaking. "Good morning, Doctor!" he said to his friend.

The scientist could not answer at once. He closed his eyes and took a deep breath. Thank God! His little friend was alive and well!

At last, once and for all, Louis Pasteur was able to erase from his mind the cries of the people of Arbois.

Character Theme—Compassion, Perseverance, & Resourcefulness

Thinking It Through

1. What event from Louis Pasteur's boyhood kept coming back to his mind?
2. In what country did Pasteur live?
3. Why did Pasteur vaccinate animals with weakened rabies' germs?
4. What animals did he use in his experiments?
5. Why did Pasteur decide to try his treatment on Joseph?

SOMETHING REALLY IMPORTANT

Lee Harrison Mountain

In the 1800s, God gave a preacher named William Booth a burden for the very poorest people of England. Booth organized the Salvation Army in the slums of London to win people to Christ. He also showed Christian love by distributing food and clothing to these extremely needy people.

William Booth's daughter Evangeline worked with him from the time she was a child. She became an outstanding musician, speaker, and writer. She was commander of the Salvation Army in the United States for 30 years, and in 1934 was elected to head up the entire worldwide ministry. Despite her talents and importance, Evangeline Booth never forgot a lesson she learned as a girl.

Evangeline Booth took off her apron when she finished her work in the kitchen.

Threading a needle quickly, she pulled a torn coat from a pile of old clothes and plunged into the next job.

"Come now, Miss Booth!" exclaimed one of her helpers. "You shouldn't be spending your precious time fixing sandwiches and patching these old clothes for the poor. You're the leader

367

of the whole Salvation Army—you should be doing something really important!"

Miss Booth glanced up at her helper and
smiled. But she kept right on sewing.

"Something really important," she repeated
to herself. The words had a familiar ring. They
brought back memories to her of the time when
she was only twelve years old.

As she sat there sewing, her mind wandered back to those days, many years ago.

Her father had just started the Salvation Army. At first Evangeline helped him enthusiastically, by collecting and then mending old clothes to give to the poor.

But as time went on, she began to get tired of these jobs. "All I ever do is patch these rags for poor people!" she had grumbled one day, kicking at a pile of old sweaters.

"Why, you're the best little helper in the world," Evangeline's father replied, paying no attention to her complaining. "Did you fix plenty of sandwiches for the prayer meeting tonight?"

"Yes," Evangeline sighed gloomily. "And I set up rows and rows of chairs in the living room. Everything's ready."

Mr. Booth patted his daughter on the shoulder. "I don't know what I'd do without you," he said.

But Evangeline shrugged. "Collecting old clothes is not *important* enough!" she cried.

"I wish I could do something really important, something like giving away a million bicycles to poor children!"

Mr. Booth chuckled. "Your heart may be in the right place, Evangeline. But sometimes I wonder about your head. You know very well that the poor people we're helping need food and clothing more than bicycles!"

But Evangeline was not at all convinced by what her father said. "Mending clothes and fixing sandwiches wouldn't be such a chore if I thought it was really important. But I can think of dozens of things I'd rather have than a sandwich or an old patched sweater."

"You wouldn't say that if you'd ever been hungry or cold," replied Mr. Booth. "Someday you'll realize just how important our gifts of clothing and food are to people who really need them. Then you won't mind doing the jobs you do to help."

The doorbell had rung while Mr. Booth was speaking, and Evangeline went to let in the first people to arrive for the prayer meeting.

Then she hurried here and there, seating the people and bringing sandwiches to them. Soon she noticed a newcomer crouched near the fireplace—a pale, cold-looking girl, clutching a basket of matches.

Evangeline picked up the sweater she had just patched and walked over to the shivering girl. "Here's a sweater for you," she said.

Smiling gratefully at Evangeline, the little

girl put on the sweater and buttoned it up, edging still closer to the fire.

Evangeline left the girl, but a few minutes later, she was back, bringing two large sandwiches. "My name's Evangeline Booth," she said, holding out the sandwiches. "What's your name?"

"Bonnie Rayburn," replied the girl.

"I'm glad that you came to Papa's prayer meeting!" Evangeline said to her. "Usually grownups are the only ones who come. Did your folks bring you with them?"

Bonnie shook her head and said, "No, I came by myself. My father is sick. He hasn't been able to work for a long time. When I heard that your father is giving things away to poor people, I came to see if it was true."

"I'm afraid you're going to be disappointed," Evangeline said. "Papa doesn't give away anything important—just food and old patched clothes."

Evangeline went on quickly as the girl's eyes brightened. "I'm sure Papa will want to do something special to help while your father is sick. He helps ever so many poor people."

The two girls sat together all through the prayer meeting. And when the people started going home, Evangeline said, in a burst of warmth,

"Stay here with me tonight, Bonnie. Tomorrow morning you can show Papa where you live, so he can take some food to your father."

Bonnie looked with longing around the warm, firelit room. "I would like to stay and visit you," she said. "But I have to sell matches tomorrow morning. That's how I make money for our breakfast. And besides, Mother would worry."

Suddenly Bonnie brightened and started moving quickly toward a woman who was on her way out. "There's Mrs. Ward!" she told Evangeline excitedly. "She lives in our building. I can ask her to tell Mother I'm spending the night with you."

The next day Evangeline awakened early. As she pushed back the covers and tested the cold floor with her big toe, she shivered.

In the bed across the room, only the top of Bonnie's head was showing above the blankets.

Evangeline started to wake her, for she had promised, the night before, not to keep Bonnie from selling her matches. But suddenly she changed her mind.

"Father says that I don't understand how the poor people suffer," she thought to herself. "This is a good time to find out. I'll let Bonnie keep on sleeping, and *I'll* go out and sell the matches!"

Quickly she wrote Bonnie a note and left it beside her on the bed. Then Evangeline put on the thin, ragged dress that Bonnie had worn. With the basket of matches on her arm, she tiptoed quietly down the stairs and let herself out through the side door.

The cold wind came rushing at Evangeline, biting through the ragged clothes she wore. Her teeth were chattering by the time she reached the corner. "I'll go back home just as soon as I earn enough money for one meal," she decided.

Soon she spotted a well-dressed man on the other side of the street. "Matches!" she cried, running over toward him. "Please buy my matches!"

"Go away child," he said crossly, hurrying away from her. "Don't be a bother."

Evangeline turned her back to the biting wind.

Two ladies in heavy, warm coats passed by. She hastened toward them, saying, "Matches, for a penny. Please buy some matches."

The two women stared at her for a moment. Then one turned to the other and said, "Imagine a child of that age selling matches in the streets!"

"It's disgraceful," answered the other. "What *can* her parents be thinking, to allow a child to beg like this?"

---

disgraceful—*bringing shame or disapproval*

They walked away.

Evangeline started rubbing her hands together. She blew on them to warm them, but even her breath did not feel warm.

Two hours later, she still had not collected enough pennies to buy a meal. She was miserably cold and weak with hunger. Her thoughts traveled longingly to the warm breakfast waiting for her at home.

As she wandered along, past a grocery store, the grocer was unpacking a big box of apples.

"Please, sir, would you sell me an apple for a few pennies?" Evangeline pleaded.

The grocer glanced at her ragged clothing, picked up an apple, and tossed it toward her. "Keep your pennies, and get going!" he shouted, before she could even thank him.

Evangeline bent her head down and hugged her arms tight against her body as she walked into the wind.

The apple was brown and soft, but she gobbled it up as if it were the sweetest fruit she had ever tasted.

After approaching a number of people and earning only a few more pennies, Evangeline decided to give up and go home.

She felt terrible, trudging back with so little money in her pocket. Certainly her few pennies would not help Bonnie much.

A block from her home, she met her father. She flung herself at him, sobbing bitterly. Then she told him what she had been trying to do.

With a gentle, loving smile, Mr. Booth put his arm around his daughter. "Evangeline," he said, "what's the most important thing in all the world to you, right this minute?"

Evangeline looked at her father blankly, wondering how he could ask her such a silly question. "I'm cold and I'm hungry!" she exclaimed sharply.

---

approach—*to go to someone in order to ask for something*

"I've never felt so wretched in my life! I'm going home to get something to eat and some warm clothes."

"But food and clothes are not really important," he said jokingly. "You told me just yesterday that you wanted to work at something *really* important!"

Evangeline bit her lip, for she realized how foolish she had sounded. "From now on, Papa," she said meekly, "whenever I fix a sandwich or patch a sweater, I'll know what an important job I'm doing."

As these memories of her childhood faded into the back of her mind, Evangeline Booth folded the clothes she had just been patching. Smiling at her helper, who was still patiently sorting a stack of old clothes, Miss Booth started back toward the Salvation Army kitchen.

"Miss Booth!" exclaimed the cook, echoing what the other helper said earlier. "You are doing too much. Why don't you leave all this mending and cooking to your helpers?"

"I guess I'm just selfish," said Miss Booth with a twinkle in her eye. "I like to keep the most important jobs in the Salvation Army for myself."

---

wretched—*miserable*

Character Theme—Compassion, Service, & Wisdom

Thinking It Through

1. What organization did Evangeline Booth's father start when she was a girl?

2. Why did Evangeline grumble about patching clothes and fixing sandwiches for the poor?

3. Why did she think that food and patched clothes were not important gifts?

4. What things did Evangeline do to help at the prayer meeting?

5. What did Evangeline do to help herself understand the sufferings of poor people? What lesson did she learn?

From the Bible

For I was an hungred, and ye gave me meat: I was thirsty, and ye gave me drink: I was a stranger, and ye took me in:

Inasmuch as ye have done it unto one of the least of these my brethen, ye have done it unto me.

—*Matthew 25:35,40*

Because of Thy Great Bounty

Because I have been given much,
    I, too, shall give;
Because of Thy great bounty, Lord,
    Each day I live
I shall divide my gifts from Thee
With every brother that I see
Who has the need of help from me.

Because I have been sheltered, fed,
    By Thy good care,
I cannot see another's lack
    And I not share
My glowing fire, my loaf of bread,
My roof's shelter overhead,
That he, too, may be comforted,

Because love has been lavished so
    Upon me, Lord,
A wealth I know that was not meant
    For me to hoard,
I shall give love to those in need,
The cold and hungry clothe and feed,
Thus shall I show my thanks indeed.

                    —Grace Noll Crowell

bounty—*generosity in giving*
lavished—*given freely and generously*
hoard—*to hide away money or goods*

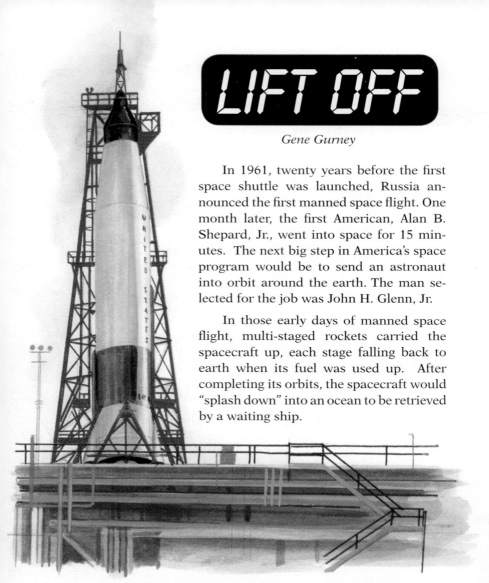

LIFT OFF

Gene Gurney

In 1961, twenty years before the first space shuttle was launched, Russia announced the first manned space flight. One month later, the first American, Alan B. Shepard, Jr., went into space for 15 minutes. The next big step in America's space program would be to send an astronaut into orbit around the earth. The man selected for the job was John H. Glenn, Jr.

In those early days of manned space flight, multi-staged rockets carried the spacecraft up, each stage falling back to earth when its fuel was used up. After completing its orbits, the spacecraft would "splash down" into an ocean to be retrieved by a waiting ship.

On February 20, 1962, American newspaper headlines told the story everyone had been waiting for:

GLENN ORBITS EARTH
THREE TIMES SAFELY.

orbit—*a path around a heavenly body*

380

After 1,160 days of hard, painstaking effort, the men of Project Mercury had achieved their goal.

There had been some discouraging setbacks during those 1,160 days, but none were more disturbing than the ones that occurred right at the end. The flight that finally proved to be so successful on February 20th had been postponed no less than ten times!

After the astrochimp Enos completed his two orbits of the earth on November 29, 1961, manned flight around the earth was next on the Project Mercury schedule. Before Enos, an unmanned capsule and the Atlas booster had performed well. There was nothing more that could be learned until a man was placed in orbit.

The man chosen to make the all-important trip was—Lieutenant Colonel John H. Glenn, Jr., at forty the oldest of the seven astronauts. His alternate, the astronaut who would go if Glenn should become ill, was Lieutenant Commander Malcolm Scott Carpenter. The date was first set for some time before the end of the year. It was hoped that, like the Soviet Union, the United States would be able to orbit a man in 1961.

---

painstaking—*very careful; diligent*
unmanned—*without people on board*
capsule—*section of the rocket that carried John Glenn*

The length of time spent in preparation between the Mercury launchings had averaged about six weeks. After Enos' flight, workers at Cape Canaveral thought that by working extra hours they could be ready in less time. But there was too much to do and too much at stake to take chances on hasty work. The date was finally set for January 16, 1962. And even that proved to be too soon.

During the pre-flight check, a defect was found in the capsule's air-conditioning system; it meant a week's delay. The repairs couldn't be completed in a week—another delay. Then there was trouble with the emergency oxygen supply to the capsule's cabin and the astronaut's pressure suit. The date of the launching had to be set back again—to January 27th.

This time the preliminary checks showed that both the Atlas and the capsule were ready to go. Astronaut Glenn, who had been training daily for the flight, was also ready. It looked as if January 27th might be the big day.

The astronaut was up at two in the morning. At 5:15 A.M. he climbed into the space capsule. The moon was shining and everything looked good for the launching.

---

preliminary—*coming before an event*

At 9:10 A.M. the flight was called off. Several minor technical difficulties had held up the countdown. While technicians worked to correct them, an unexpected cloud cover rolled in over Cape Canaveral. It was thick and it showed no signs of lifting. Project Mercury officials would not be able to follow the Atlas as it lifted off the pad. The safety of the astronaut depended on optical as well as electronic tracking.

"Well, there'll be another day," said the weary Colonel Glenn as he left the launching pad after four hours in the capsule.

As it turned out, there were to be several more days. Fuel had leaked into an insulated bulkhead of the Atlas missile. The insulation had to be replaced. And then the weather caused more delays. Like Astronauts Shepard and Grissom before him, Glenn would land in the Atlantic, and weather is usually bad in the mid-Atlantic during February. A series of storms moved across the area. The waiting recovery ships pitched and rolled in strong winds and waves twenty feet high. A capsule landing in such seas was likely to be lost.

The storms continued to move in. Cape Canaveral and the whole country continued to wait.

---

optical—*visual; having to do with the sense of sight*
bulkhead—*a partition separating compartments inside the rocket*

The Atlas booster and the capsule stood on Pad 14 ready to go.

Astronaut Glenn went over his flight procedures again and again. Project Mercury was close to achieving its goal. Everything depended on the weather.

During the days of waiting, there were some who said Project Mercury was being too cautious; the officials were too insistent that everything be super-safe. "All progress involves some risk," they said. "Lindbergh would never have crossed the Atlantic if he had been flying for Project Mercury."

But Mercury officials refused to take any chances. Their job was to send a man into space and into orbit, and then bring him safely back to earth. They wanted to learn if a man could carry out useful activities while traveling in space. No activity could be useful if the man didn't come back safely.

There was another reason why Project Mercury was proceeding cautiously. None of its activities were being kept secret. The whole world could watch, and was watching, what happened at Cape Canaveral. The Soviet Union had already

booster—*the rocket that carried the capsule into orbit*
procedures—*the way something is to be done*
proceeding—*going on; moving along*

384

sent two men into orbit around the earth. Now it was the turn of the United States. Failure would mean a serious loss of prestige.

The sky was covered with clouds when John Glenn was awakened at 2:20 on the morning of February 20, 1962. Although the weather didn't look encouraging, out at the launch area the final countdown had begun at 11:30 P.M. Breakfast was at 2:45 A.M.—orange juice, scrambled eggs, steak, and toast. The same menu had been prepared for astronauts Shepard and Grissom, and for Glenn himself, on January 27th.

The physical examination, which started at 3:00 A.M., lasted an hour. In spite of the weary days of waiting, the astronaut was in excellent shape. And so were the Atlas and the capsule. The countdown was proceeding without a hitch.

At 4:00 A.M. the count was stopped at T minus 120 minutes. This was a planned hold to give the technicians some extra time if they needed it. So far everything was right on schedule. By 4:30 Astronaut Glenn was getting into his twenty-pound space suit. Pressure tests to make sure the suit would hold oxygen were next.

---

prestige—*a high level of honor among others*
T minus 120 minutes—*two hours before launch*
hold—*a temporary delay*

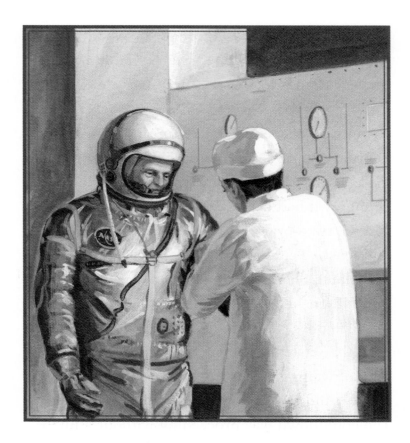

At 5:00 A.M. he was ready to leave Hangar S
for the launching area. It was still cloudy. Astronaut Carpenter and the flight surgeon rode to
Pad 14 with Glenn. Pad 14 was ablaze with lights.
After the astronauts arrived, the hold was extended
for 45 minutes. Trouble had been discovered in
the guidance system of the Atlas booster.

At 6:00 A.M. Glenn left the van that had
brought him from Hangar S. Crewmen working
in the launching area could see him smile behind

his space visor as he walked briskly to the elevator. There had been some breaks in the clouds, but they had closed in again. Above the capsule, which had been named Friendship 7, the sky was black and forbidding.

The countdown was resumed at 6:26—T minus 120. The astronaut was in the capsule and the hatch was closed, but he couldn't be sealed in. There was a broken bolt on the hatch cover. The bolt had to be replaced. It was now 7:25—T minus 60 and holding. The sky was still covered with clouds.

And so it went with the hands of the clock getting ever closer to 9:00. There was growing concern about the time. Unless Friendship 7 could be launched before 9:30 or 9:45, its orbits would have to be reduced to two or even to one. For a safe recovery, there had to be an ample margin of daylight left in the Atlantic landing area.

At 9:30 A.M. the count had reached T minus 15 minutes. Both the astronaut in the capsule and the Mercury officials were reporting all systems, "Go." The clouds that had hung over the Cape were gone. A beautiful sun was shining, and a feeling of hope had replaced the earlier gloom.

---

ample margin—*enough time*

After just one more short delay, the count was resumed for the last time at 9:42. When the clock moved past 9:46, the count was in seconds: 9 . . ., 8 . . ., 7 . . ., 6 . . ., 5 . . ., 4 . . ., 3 . . ., 2 . . ., 1 . . ., 0!

Fire and smoke appeared under the tail of the Atlas. The 130-ton rocket rose slowly from the launching pad trailing a bright, white-yellow flame. With a roar it went streaking skyward followed by a thin, white vapor trail. Within seconds it was gone.

From his capsule perched on top of the speeding Atlas, Astronaut Glenn reported: "Lift off, the clock is operating, we're under way."

Friendship 7 was moving toward its orbital altitude. As he rocketed through the area where there was still enough atmosphere to buffet the capsule, the astronaut told the Control Center: "Some vibration area coming up here now."

But he was having no trouble. All his instruments were working and he was reporting their readings to the Control Center in a calm, steady voice. The man who was receiving his messages was Alan Shepard, the astronaut whose ride in the capsule Freedom 7 had made him the United States' first spaceman.

From the moment of launching, the men in the Control Center had been greatly concerned with the flight path of the Atlas. Any change from the planned direction would send the capsule into an orbit over areas where it could not be tracked and where it would be difficult to recover after landing. Likewise, the capsule's speed had to be just right. If it didn't reach a speed close to 17,500 miles an hour at the proper point, it wouldn't go into orbit at all and would have to be brought down at once. Too much speed, on the other hand, would result in an unplanned orbit that might expose the astronaut to dangerous

---

altitude—*height above sea level or above the earth's surface*
buffet—*to beat against*

radiation. And when the capsule came down, it might be out of reach of the recovery forces.

The two booster engines of the Atlas had exhausted their fuel two minutes after the launching, leaving the 60,000-pound thrust sustainer engine to lift the capsule into orbit. After five minutes of flight it, too, burned out, and Friendship 7 went into orbit at 17,545 miles an hour.

Computers at the Goddard Space Flight Center at Greenbelt, Maryland, had been electronically following the Atlas since it was one-half of one inch off the launching pad. Within 2½ seconds after the capsule went into orbit, information on its speed, elevation, and direction had been sent to Goddard, run through the computers there, and the results sent to the Cape. It was a good orbit!

From the Mercury Control Center, Alan Shepard relayed the happy news to Glenn in Friendship 7. "You have a go. At least seven orbits."

That meant that the orbit attained by Friendship 7 was good enough to carry it seven times around the earth. The plan, however, called for it to come down after three trips.

Upon going into orbit, Friendship 7 had turned around so that its blunt end was forward. This enabled Glenn to look back toward Cape Canaveral.

---

exhausted their fuel—*used all their fuel*

Like Gagarin, Titov, Shepard, and Grissom—all of whom had traveled in space before him—the astronaut was greatly impressed with what he saw below him. There was a big cloud pattern stretching all the way to Florida. "Oh, that view is tremendous!" he exclaimed.

Gagarin (gə·gär′yĭn)—*Russian cosmonaut; first man to orbit the earth*
Titov (tē′täf)—*Russian cosmonaut; second man to orbit the earth*

Character Theme—Determination & Perseverance

Thinking It Through

1. How many times did John Glenn orbit the earth?
2. Where was he to land?
3. What was the name of Glenn's space capsule?
4. Why was it important for the space capsule to reach just the right speed?

Credits

All reasonable effort has been made to trace owner of copyright materials in this book, but in some instances this has proven impossible. The publisher will be glad to receive information leading to more complete acknowledgments in subsequent printings of the book, and in the meantime extends apologies for any omissions.

"Andy Stands Guard" Excerpt from *Young Hickory* by Stanley Young. Copyright 1940 by Stanley Young. Reprinted by permission of Henry Holt and Company.

"Battle with Death" from *Men of Science* by Dorothy Haas, illustrated by J. L. Pellicer, copyright © 1959, renewed 1987 by Random House, Inc. Used by permission of Golden Books, an imprint of Random House Children's Books, a division of Random House, Inc.

"Because of Thy Great Bounty" from *Poems of Inspiration and Courage* by Grace Noll Crowell. Copyright 1928, 1934 by Harper & Row Publishers, Inc., Renewed 1956, 1962 by Grace Noll Crowell. Reprinted by permission of HarperCollins Publishers.

"Captain Cook" From *Mr. Popper's Penguins* by Richard and Florence Atwater. Copyright ©1938 by Florence Atwater and Richard Atwater; Copyright © renewed 1966 by Florence Atwater, Doris Atwater, and Carroll Atwater Bishop. By permission of Little Brown & Company.

"Cats" copyright ©1957 by Eleanor Farjeon. Reprinted by permission of Harold Ober Associates Incorporated.

"Citronella Weather" by Mildred Lawrence, copyright 1946, copyright renewed 1974 by Random House, Inc., from *Story Parade*. Used by permission of Golden Books.

"A Dragon-fly," "Farms," "Knowledge," "Mary Indoors," copyright 1933, 1961 by Eleanor Farjeon. Reprinted by permission of Harold Ober Associates Incorporated.

"The Elephant" from *Complete Verse* by Hilaire Belloc (Copyright © The Estate of Hilaire Belloc 1970) is reproduced by permission PFD (www.pfd.co.uk) on behalf of the Estate of Hilaire Belloc.

"Furry Bear" From *Now We Are Six* by A. A. Milne, illustrated by E. H. Shepard, copyright 1927 by E. P. Dutton, renewed ©1955 by A. A. Milne. Used by permission of Dutton Children's Books, a Division of Penguin Young Readers Group, a Member of Penguin Group (USA) Inc., 345 Hudson Street, New York, NY 10014. All rights reserved. © Trustees of the Pooh Properties. Published by Egmont UK Limited, London and used with permission. Line Illustrations Copyright © The Estate of E. H. Shepard reproduced with permission of Curtis Brown Group Limited, London.

"The Greatest River in the World" Excerpt from *Mark Twain: His Life* by Catherine Owens Peare. Copyright 1954 by Catherine Owens Peare. Reprinted by permission of Henry Holt and Company.

"Habits of the Hippopotamus" from *Gaily the Troubadour* by Arthur Guiterman. Reprinted by permission of Richard E. Sclove.

"The Heart Test" by Sandra Klaus reprinted by permission of the author.

"Lift Off" from *Americans into Orbit* by Gene Gurney, copyright ©1962 by Gene Gurney. Used by permission of Random House Children's Books, a division of Random House, Inc.

"Little Georgie Sings a Song", from *Rabbit Hill* by Robert Lawson, copyright 1944 by Robert Lawson. Renewed copyright © 1971 by John W. Boyd. Used by permission of Viking Penguin, A Division of Penguin Young Readers Group, A Member of Penguin Group (USA) Inc., 345 Hudson Street, New York, NY 10014. All rights reserved.

"The Middle Bear" from *The Middle Moffat*, copyright 1942 and renewed 1970 by Eleanor Estes. Reprinted by permission of Harcourt, Inc.

"The Old Injun Trail" by Lillie V. Albrecht, copyright 1949, copyright renewed 1977 by Random House, Inc., from *Story Parade*. Used by permission of Golden Books.

"Paul Bunyan, Northwoods Lumberman" from *Tall Tale America* by Walter Blair, ©1944, 1987 by Walter Blair. Reprinted by permission of The University of Chicago Press, Chicago.

"Seal" from *Laughing Time: Collected Nonsense* by William Jay Smith. Copyright © 1990 by William Jay Smith. Reprinted by permission of Farrar, Straus, and Giroux, LLC.

"Something Really Important" by Lee Harrison Mountain from *Frontier to Explore* in *Golden Rule Series* by Leavell, et al. Copyright ©1964 by American Book Company. Reprinted by permission of Houghton Mifflin Company. All rights reserved.

"Stopping by Woods on a Snowy Evening" from *The Poetry of Robert Frost* edited by Edward Connery Lathem, published by Jonathan Cape. Copyright 1923, 1969 by Henry Holt and Company. Copyright 1951 by Robert Frost. Reprinted by permission of Henry Holt and Company, LLC and The Random House Group Ltd.

"A Story in the Snow" by Pearl Riggs Crouch, from *Wee Wisdom*, January 1931. Used by permission of Unity School of Christianity.

"Tall Bram of Little Pigeon" by Manly Wade Wellman reprinted by permission of Mr. Dave Drake (first published in *Boy's Life*, 1947).

"We Invent the Franklin Stove" from *Ben and Me* by Robert Lawson. Copyright © 1939 by Robert Lawson; Copyright © renewed 1967 by John W. Boyd. By permission of Little Brown & Company.

"Whitey and the Jinglebob" by Glen Rounds, copyright 1946, copyright renewed 1974 by Random House, Inc., from *Story Parade*. Used by permission of Golden Books.

"Wilbur Meets Charlotte" from *Charlotte's Web* by E. B. White, illustrated by Garth Williams (Hamish Hamilton, 1952). Copyright 1952 by E. B. White. Text copyright renewed ©1980 by E. B. White. Illustrations copyright renewed ©1980 by Garth Williams. Used by permission of Harper-Collins Publishers. Reproduced by permission of Penguin Books Ltd.

"The Willow Basket" by Carol Ryrie Brink. Reprinted with the permission of Simon & Schuster for Young Readers, an imprint of Simon & Schuster Children's Publishing Division, from *Magical Melons*, More Stories about Caddie Woodlawn by Carol Ryrie Brink. Copyright ©1939, 1940, 1944 by The Macmillan Company. Copyright © renewed 1967, 1968, 1972 by Carol Ryrie Brink. All rights reserved.